If we care about our own survival, we must learn to live in harmony with the land and its resources.
We must become *users* of the resources of this planet and no longer think of ourselves as *consumers*.

THE USER'S GUIDE gives specific information to the reader on the ways in which he must change; the daily decisions he can make that will improve or deteriorate his environment—which household cleansers contribute the most pollution and which the least, what effects excess packaging has, and what products should be done away with completely.

The User's Guide To The Protection Of The Environment

PAUL SWATEK

A FRIENDS OF THE EARTH/BALLANTINE BOOK
An Intext Publisher
NEW YORK

FRIENDS OF THE EARTH, founded in 1969 by David Brower, is a non-profit membership organization streamlined for legislative activity in the United States and abroad which is aimed at restoring the environment misused by man and at preserving remaining wilderness where the life force continues to flow freely.

FRIENDS OF THE EARTH, in order to fight without restrictions, does not wish to be tax-deductible, and for that reason has special need for and invites your participation.

Table 7 courtesy of the National Audubon Society
Table 39 courtesy of the Union Oil Company

FRIENDS OF THE EARTH
30 East 42nd Street
New York, N.Y. 10017

451 Pacific Avenue
San Francisco, California 94133

917 15th Street, N.W.
Washington, D.C. 20005

1372 Kapiolani Blvd.
Honolulu, Hawaii 96814

P.O. Box 1977
Anchorage, Alaska 99501

BALLANTINE BOOKS, INC.
101 Fifth Avenue, New York, N.Y. 10003

In Case You Have Any Doubts

How do we know that we face an environmental crisis? Anyone not yet convinced that we do should immediately put down this book and open his senses. Go to the nearest river and decide whether you would want to drink its water or swim in it. Look at the sky and see whether it is blue or brown. Know that Lake Erie has aged 15,000 years since 1920 and that blue whales, leopards, and polar bears are increasingly rare.

We are simplifying our ecosystem and tampering with its checks and balances. Exactly what all of this means for the future is not clear. Man himself may now be an endangered species. Think about it.

> The real specter that pollution casts over man's future is not, perhaps, the extinction of Homo sapiens but his mutation into some human equivalent of the carp now lurking in Lake Erie's fetid depths, living off poison.

> —*Newsweek,* January 26, 1970

Contents

1. INTRODUCTION

1. Introduction

HOW DOES THE CONSUMER FIT IN?

Every consumer decision you make has an environmental impact. This is an ecological fact of life. Every time you visit the supermarket, buy a ticket to travel, choose a place to live, your choices have an effect, for better or worse, on the quality of the air you breathe and the water you drink—on the world you experience with your eyes and ears and nose.

These connections are not always obvious, but we're getting better at recognizing them. Clearly the paper we buy as packaging and throw away was once forest. And the electric power that flows silently from the wall sockets ultimately comes from a hydroelectric dam, a fossil fuel plant, or a nuclear reactor. Recently we have also become aware that phosphates in the detergents we use to wash our clothes and dishes have contributed in a major way to the "death" of our lakes and rivers. Lake Erie has virtually died for our sins. We have recognized that the automobile, cause of most of our urban air pollution, must also bear a fair share of the blame for the oil leak at Union Oil's Platform A in California's Santa Barbara Channel. We have learned that there is a link between DDT use and the dying-out of the peregrine falcon and many other predators which are at the end of long food chains, and we know that we, too, are at the end of a long food chain. We also have good reason to believe that the psychological effects of crowding, noise, and filth are major causes of urban social unrest.

It isn't hard to become good at spotting these connections, but when one begins to realize the magnitude of such problems as the death of Lake Erie, the extinction of entire species of animals, and the terrible threat implicit in air pollution, the significance of the decisions that an individual can make tends to pale in comparison with the significance of those made by industry and government. At this point, however, it is well to remember that although each of us is only one individual, there are millions of us, and although government and industry may seem monolithic, they are, after all, merely collections of individuals. The fight to preserve a place on Earth for man must seek first to transform people, and then through them their institutions. Besides, what easier place is there to start than with yourself?

> There is another benefit to individual action. It is our only insurance against government inaction, or, should it become necessary, government dictatorship. Waiting for government "to do something" can be like waiting for Godot. Too often the result is too little too late. At any rate, eco-survival may be too important an issue to entrust to any public body, particularly the ones that must share a major responsibility for the present hazardous state. We should be interdependent with, but not dependent upon government.
>
> — Ted Radke in *Ecology*

YOUR BEST GUIDE IS COMMON SENSE

The most valuable guide that any consumer can use in making his consumer decisions count is common sense. This is especially true today because of the rapidly changing situation in which we find ourselves. There is clearly an exploding public awareness of environmental problems. As with most such explosions of knowledge, we actually find ourselves facing expanding frontiers of ignorance; that is, the more knowledge we acquire, the more unanswered questions we realize there are. In response to this bewildering array of problems and crises there has been an equally bewildering array of "solutions," some valid, others not. It has never been more true that one cannot believe everything one reads in the newspapers, especially the advertisements.

It is difficult to get "the facts" and even harder to verify them. This is true not just for the concerned consumer, but even for the compiler of a consumer's guide, for corporations and governmental regulatory agencies maintain a policy of secrecy that leaves communication of information up to public relations men in the first instance and politicians in the second. These people too often have neither the technical background nor, unfortunately, the freedom from financial interest to enable them to communicate information accurately.

Another problem is that "the facts" are constantly changing. This is especially true of product formulations. Take detergents as an example. Several years ago a box of detergent contained materials that were not biodegradable. These began to accumulate in such large amounts that streams, rivers, and groundwater became choked with suds. Around 1965, the hue and cry from outraged conservationists and other water users caused the detergent manufacturers to modify all of their formulations, and today all detergents are biodegradable. However, today's detergents have also been "improved" by adding enzymes and escalating the levels of phosphates. Once again the product has become suspect. When detergent manufacturers introduce new formulations of a product, they seldom change its name. Thus, unless there is a simple way for the consumer to learn the ingredients of what he is buying—from the label, for example—he cannot make an informed choice without special inquiry. He may also still have to make special inquiries about some of the products listed in the tables in this book, which, of course, cannot change with time nor include all regional variations.

What then can the consumer, faced with many uncertainties and without special technical knowledge, do? He can try to learn more about the environmental impact of the products he buys and, while so doing, maintain a healthy skepticism about the sources of his information. This means, for instance, recognizing the bias that such firms as General Motors Corporation, Chevron Oil Company, Ethyl Corporation (manufacturer of tetraethyl lead), and the catalytic muffler manufacturers will each bring to the debate over how much it will cost to make the switch to unleaded gasoline. It also means keeping in mind the vested interests of the Automobile Manufacturer's Association and the American Petroleum Institute. Even the professional societies, ideally supposed to be objective and careful in making judgments, frequently represent narrow points of view in their public news releases and trade journals.

Unfortunately, government has too often failed to live up to its role of impartial protector of the public interest. In a sense, this failing is built into our system of representative government. A congressman from Texas or Louisiana is expected to have different views on the oil import quota system than one from oil-poor New England. Beyond this, however, one should recognize that "our" representatives represent more than just us—business, industry, labor, and parts of the governmental bureaucracy compete as constituents and often have a more direct line to your elected officials than you do. This is especially true of governmental regulatory agencies, which have in too many cases become advocates for the regulatees.

These generalizations are not meant to imply that all industry and government sources are unreliable. Many are genuinely concerned about the welfare of the general public and about the environmental consequences of the decisions they make. These points are made because you, as a consumer of goods and services, also become a user of information. You must size up your sources of information as you would the salesman who tries to sell you a used car.

Where *can* the consumer, worried about the deteriorating quality of his environment, turn for information? This is where the common sense comes in. The buyer must think for himself. Compare what business leaders say in speeches about pollution with what their companies' advertisements advocate. Even the "bad guys" frequently let slip very useful information when buttressing their own arguments. Try drawing your own conclusions from their data. It's fun, especially when your reasoning is right and theirs is wrong.

Another thing you can do is to insist on knowing the facts. When ingredients are listed on a package label, take the time to read it. In this way you can spot such things as harmful food additives or hard pesticides in a can of bug spray. When the information isn't on the label, as, for example, phosphate levels in detergents are not, tell the store manager and the manufacturer that you want to know. If they don't hear you and thousands of others with the same demand, a politician or Ralph Nader probably will.

The emergence of the consumer advocate and the rejuvenation of the muckraking journalist and the reform politician have brought new hope and new sources of information. Ralph Nader's careful exposés of the automobile industry and his more recent work in other consumer and environmental fields has done a lot to bring new facts before the public and has obviously had an impact on the nature of the products that the consumer can buy. In the flood of new books, newspaper reports, and magazine articles on the environmental crisis there is a wealth of practical information. And to illustrate the good work that some legislators are doing, one can point to Congressman Henry Reuss of Wisconsin, who has been largely responsible for the control of detergent pollution that has been achieved to date.

The battle is also being waged in the courts, where the Environmental Defense Fund, the Sierra Club, FOE, and others are forcing careful examination of environmental issues. Additionally, a growing number of scientists and other professionals are coming down out of their ivory towers, and they are being heard.

Although the workings of both man's technology and nature's systems are complex, many of the problems that have arisen from the collision between them have distressingly simple roots. "Any fool can see" that building a home on the side of an unstable cliff is risky, yet some Southern Californians continue to do it. Nor is a Ph.D. required to understand that our solid waste problems arise from excess packaging and not enough recycling. It doesn't require special training to keep a broad perspective and to apply common sense.

Thus, for every technically knowledgeable Barry Commoner, René Dubos, George Wald, and Ian McHarg there is a layman activist such as David Brower, a Congressman Reuss, an Arthur Godfrey. In fact, the technologist's training can stand in his way. There is a growing awareness that civilized man has blindly followed the technologists into a mess. They, we, you must start rethinking. And while we question the basic assumptions that underlie our American life style and rethink our technology, we should look to the understanding of natural systems that ecologists have been gaining. For we know that man is fallible; the same adjective isn't applied to nature.

LEARN THAT YOU CAN SAY NO

Think for a moment about what it means to be an American. Statistics indicate that the population of motor vehicles is now over 100 million, that there is a television set in 98.5% of all homes that have electricity, and that each of us is supplied, on the average, with 3200 calories per day and 237 pounds of meat in a year. Collectively, Americans travel more than a trillion miles each year. Our standard of living is reflected in our ever-expanding gross national product and our ever-increasing per capita consumption of such commodities as beef, plastics, transportation, appliances, and energy.

> Our crowding is not basically a matter of too many human beings to the square mile but of the enormous retinue of energy and material that accompanies each of us. Like King Lear with his hundred riotous knights and squires, we strain the hospitality of our dwelling space, and from

our situation, as from Lear's, much grief may follow.

—Max Ways, *Fortune,* Feb., 1970

As the population has grown and, much more important, as per capita consumption has increased, being an American has also meant enduring interminable traffic jams, foul air, crowded cities (and national parks), deteriorating public services, and mounting levels of noise, solid wastes, and pesticide residues.

There is an approved American way of doing things that has produced a high degree of freedom from material want and, simultaneously, a crescendo of crises that threaten not only this freedom but most of our other freedoms as well. Social custom teaches us to strive for a privately owned, single-family home in the suburbs, possessing a garage of at least two-car capacity, and filled with "conveniences" that assure us of more "leisure" time. Advertising urges us to consume and dispose. We spend much of our free time as spectators watching professional performers or in vigorous activity behind the wheel of some power-driven machine—a car, boat, or snowmobile. Life is kinetic and frantic.

Is this really what you want? The decision is yours and you are free to say no.

However, it is certainly not that easy for the individual to do much about the more far-reaching problems, such as smog, urban sprawl, or low levels of pesticide and radioactive contamination. What people *can* control is the extent to which their individual actions contribute to these major collective problems. This is important, because *it is the escalation of per capita consumption,* more than mere increase in our numbers, that has so adversely affected the quality of our environment.

This book presents some of the options that are open to you as a consumer and attempts to look beyond the present practices and the extrapolations that advertisers would have us consider. Some of the options hark back to the past, others look to the future, and still others come from foreign cultures. This book tries to assess their impact on environmental quality, to go beyond dollar costs and benefits to include the social costs and benefits that have heretofore been ignored. Many of the conclusions will be new.

The challenge to the concerned consumer will be to say no to the custom-sanctioned behavior that has brought us near to ecocatastrophe. If you can learn to say no to increasing your consumption of electric power, you will be saying yes to cleaner air (less sulfur dioxide) and to an intact Grand Canyon (with no dams). If you can say no to purchasing larger and larger cars, you will be saying no to smog and traffic congestion and highways that fragment city and countryside.

Some of the consumer decisions you make obviously have greater impact on environmental quality than others. The challenge is to avoid the dual tendency to downgrade the significance of the minor decisions while succumbing to selfish considerations when the obviously important ones are made. The battle for environmental quality must take on some of the aspects of a religion. Avoid the hypocrisy that selectively applies the tenets only to some parts of your life and not to others.

The ecological approach to environmental problems requires that we work through both the individual and his institutions—commerce, industry, and government. We buy and consume and dispose. We also vote, pay taxes, manage businesses, and complain to our public officials. Although the focus of this handbook is you, the consumer, understand that your dollar vote alone will not be enough. If you are willing to make your dollar vote yes for responsibility, however, the chance that you and your children can avoid ecocatastrophe is that much increased.

GENERAL CONSIDERATIONS

Some words

Before going any further, let's take a look at a few words. Some of them may be new; familiar ones may be viewed in a new light.

Environment. Generally speaking, environment is everything—physical and otherwise—that surrounds us. Since we experience it with our eyes and ears, for example, we speak of a visual environment and an aural environment. Since we respond to it aesthetically, we should also think of an aesthetic environment.

Ecology. Ecology has been around for a long time as a science, a science that has examined the ways in which plants and animals relate to each other and to their physical environments. However, it is no longer possible to view ecology as being concerned only with Venus's-fly-traps and flies or with frogs and lily pads, because suddenly man has discovered that he, too, is a part of the ecological system.

Ecosystems. Living things that relate to each other as predators or by sharing food or living space are said to be part of an ecosystem. In stable ecosystems, interrelationships among the different members work out so that each mutually supports the continued existence of the other members and the system. A woodland meadow, a puddle of rainwater, Lake Erie, and your own digestive tract are all ecosystems. The ultimate ecosystem man is likely to have to deal with is the solar system.

Interdependence. The various ecosystems are themselves interdependent—if one is disturbed, adjustments may be required in others that seem far removed.

Stability. In spaceships, man builds backup systems to guard against mishaps. Nature, too, adds complexity to her life-support systems to obtain adaptability and stability. Simplifying an ecosystem, as man does in mass-production agriculture, for instance, makes the system more vulnerable, in this case to a pest invasion.

Ecological Cycles. Natural systems tend to order themselves so that the wastes of one member are the food for another. In this way the resources of the system are conserved. Thus, plants turn carbon dioxide into oxygen which, in turn, gets used by animals to burn up their food, a process which regenerates the carbon dioxide.

Biodegradability. Man has created a large number of substances which were not previously found in the natural world, and he produces others in such quantities as never occurred before. Those which break down rapidly on their own or through the action of organisms are termed biodegradable. Others are so unnatural that the organisms that live on this planet have no way of chewing them up. Such long-lasting, non-biodegradable products as DDT, plastics, and aluminum cans present problems when they interact adversely with living things or accumulate to the point that they take up too much space.

Non-renewable Resources. Man lives on a planet with finite resources. That is to say, he has so much land and clean water, so much oxygen, so much tin, and no more. The planet contains large but not unlimited quantities of coal and oil (the so-called fossil fuels) and high-grade mineral ores.

Recycling. When natural mechanisms for bringing one of man's waste products back into an ecological cycle do not exist, man must devise a way of recycling it or ultimately he will have to forego further use of that resource. He chops down trees to make fiber, out of which he makes paper. Unless used paper is repulped and made into new paper, more trees have to be cut. By recovering scrap metal from junk piles he can reduce the amount of ore he takes out of the Earth. Some materials, such as plastics, can be recycled only by burning them. (In this case, the ecological loop is closed back to the natural through CO_2 and photosynthesis.)

Energy. When we consider the planet Earth as man's ecosystem, energy turns out to be the one renewable resource. Ultimately this energy comes from the sun. The life-support system that has evolved on this planet, with its cycles and interdependent ecosystems, provides the mechanisms by which the energy in sunlight gets trapped (photosynthesis) and distributed throughout the system. Man needs this energy to make his muscles move, to generate heat to keep him warm and to cook his food, to transport him from place to place, and to run his industries. Because energy is the ultimate resource, other resources are often measured in terms of it.

Pollution. In a broad sense, pollution is anything that

interferes with the proper functioning of the ecosystem. It can include many naturally occurring materials as well as such unnatural substances as DDT and nuclear fallout. Phosphates and nitrates, essential in low concentrations as nutrients, pollute lakes and rivers in the high concentrations that sewage treatment plants and agricultural runoff produce. Water released from a cooling tower as a fog that interferes with visibility on a highway must also be considered a pollutant. Noise pollution, sustained at more than 80 decibels, can cause physiological as well as psychological effects.

Some ecological principles

There are a few ecological facts of life which should be kept in mind as you read this book and try to apply its ideas.

Everything comes from somewhere and everything ends up somewhere. While this may hardly come as a shock, neither has it served many of us as a guiding principle. Modern man's failure to keep it in mind has begun to plague him.

Some of the animal behaviorists trace this human fault back to the apes, who live in trees and can let their excrement and litter drop into the void below. Compare their behavior to that of the contemporary litterbug. Even the responsible citizen flushes most of his waste down a toilet or drain or throws it into a trash can that gets emptied by the sanitation department. Out of sight, out of mind.

The problem is especially severe with the urban dweller, for he is even more remote from his sources of supply than he is from the sewers that absorb his waste. Water flows in apparently unlimited quantities out of a faucet; food comes prepared and packaged from the local supermarket. He never has to worry about the three pounds of cow manure that gets produced out on the farm for every quart of milk he brings home. Once he had to haul coal and hoard his supply of lamp oil. Now his energy supply flows silently into the home through pipes and wires. Beyond a monthly or bimonthly bill, the consumer has little incentive to conserve. Thus, it is small wonder that there is a severe waste problem that is threatening our land and water resources.

Modern technology has isolated us not only from the natural life-support system, but also from technology's own pollution. How many people know what product was being made at the Dow and Wyandotte chemical plants that poisoned Lake St. Clair and Lake Erie with mercury?

As with the mercury poisoning that went undetected for a substantial period of time, many forms of technological pollution act insidiously. We dump sulfur dioxide (SO_2) and DDT and radioactivity into our environment and count on dilution to protect us, but some of these contaminants concentrate in certain living things, while others work more subtle damage at subacute levels. Lakes "die" and birds lay eggs with shells too thin to sustain life.

All systems and problems are ultimately if not intimately interrelated. It is important that this principle be kept in mind, because steps that are taken to solve one problem tend to have consequences that spill over into other areas. Technology, which has been successful largely through the technique of focusing attention on limited problems, has a distressing tendency to ignore this principle. Thus, incineration of wastes aggravates air pollution and primary treatment of sewage brings on the eutrophication, or "death," of lakes and waterways.

To be valid, technical solutions to environmental problems must be based on an appreciation of the complexity of the relevant ecosystems and must attack the root causes, not the symptoms. To illustrate, man dumps most of his sewage into watercourses at the same time that he is mining minerals and fixing nitrogen from the air to replenish the soil. If, instead, this so-called "waste" were returned to the soil as the fertilizer that it is, the poisoning of our waters with artificial fertilizer runoff and their subsequent eutrophication could be alleviated.

The automobile offers a dramatic illustration of this interrelatedness. Consider the major polluting industries.

Petroleum, steel, mining, rubber, textiles, cement, and plastics are all clearly related to the automobile. Consider also air pollution, congestion of the courts with liability claims, urban noise and traffic jams, the asphalt syndrome, and highways that destroy cityscape and countryside. Striking a blow at this monster obviously will have wide-ranging effects.

In similar ways one sees that the open space, food, population, and pollution crises are inextricably tied up with urban decay, poverty, crime, and war. It doesn't make sense to squabble over which crisis is most urgent. The practice of trying to tackle problems one by one is both obsolete and ecologically unsound.

We live on a planet whose resources are finite. During the several centuries it took for civilization to spread across the North American continent, it appeared that the resources of land and water and minerals were inexhaustible. This was how modern society's attitude toward its resource base was shaped. Kenneth Boulding has characterized this attitude with the term "cowboy economy." Air and water were common property and could be treated as the individual wished. Homesteaders and prospectors had the run of public lands, and anyone who wanted to develop land or marsh was allowed to do so. At the same time the notion of the sanctity of private property grew.

Some time ago the country bumped up against the Pacific Ocean, and since then the empty spaces have been filling up to the point that men now speak of "megalopolises," giant urban belts sprawling from Boston to Washington, from Milwaukee to Pittsburgh, and from Santa Barbara to San Diego. More recently man has witnessed the fact that the capacity of the air and water to absorb the byproducts of his high standard of living has been exceeded, first in Los Angeles, then in Lake Erie, and now in countless locations across the land.

Men still place faith, however, in the infiniteness of the Earth's resources. The ocean will continue to absorb all of the sewage we pump into it and, at the same time, provide new sources of enormous quantities of food. We plan to use as much as one half of the water in our rivers and streams to absorb waste heat from power generation while this process adds more carbon dioxide to the atmosphere by burning more and more fossil fuels. The use of water as a coolant for nuclear plants may be even greater while creating hazards only guessed at at present. The fact is we have badly overharvested many of the commercially important ocean fish. The ecologically important marshes and wetlands have been so drastically reduced by drive-in movie theaters, housing tracts, and shopping center parking lots that populations of fish are decreasing. And scientists continue to worry about the long-term effects of excess heat and carbon dioxide on world climate.

Nature has spent literally millions of years refining a stable ecosystem. Her systems are complex and, precisely because of their complexity, they are able to absorb a great many of man's insults.

The most sophisticated computer models that men have devised can only roughly simulate the complex interactions and feedback networks of nature's simplest systems, let alone the ecology of a river under pollution stress. The scientific method isolates and focuses attention on subsystems. It thus tends to generate oversimplified solutions, and also leads man to try to simplify his environment so that he can better "control" it. In so doing, he makes the environment more vulnerable to the natural stresses and human miscalculations that are bound to occur.

Based on its recent track record, it would probably be wise to rein in technology until the technologists gain a better understanding of how their systems are interacting with natural systems. There is a vast inner frontier behind the leading edge of modern technology that begs for exploration. It is more than likely that many of the practices man has developed to control the environment for his betterment have alternatives which are more ecologically sound. Biological control of insect pests offers an alternative to chemical control, to give one example. More often than not it makes sense to work with nature.

If the decision is made, instead, to forge ahead, blindly

assaulting the natural life-support systems as we have been doing, we can expect only disaster. Nature fights back, and her weapons are floods, killer smogs, pest invasions, famine, and conflict.

Our civilization has moved into a new era in which certain traditional freedoms and privileges—unfettered private ownership, unlimited family size, total mobility in high-powered cars—collide head on with the ecological facts of life. There isn't any choice in the matter. Either men voluntarily control themselves, have their governments impose controls, or nature will do it with ecocatastrophe.

> Modern man can adapt biologically to the technological environment only insofar as mechanisms of adaptation are potentially present in his genetic code. For this reason, we can almost take it for granted that he cannot achieve successful biological adaptation to insults with which he has had no experience in his evolutionary past, such as the shrill noises of modern equipment, the exhausts of automobiles and factories, the countless new synthetic products that get into air, water, and food.
> —René Dubos, *The Environmental Handbook*.

The human animal evolved in an environment that was filled with green vegetation, blue skies and oceans, and thousands of other living creatures. Eminent scientists warn modern man that a decent natural environment may be a necessary element in his continued psychological well-being. The many polls that have been taken at the entry to the decade of the '70s indicate that men agree, for green grass and clean air consistently rank at the top of things that people most value.

Some economics

As a consumer concerned with environmental quality, you ought to be familiar with a few economic facts of life.

You live in a market economy wherein goods and services are assigned prices which are supposed to reflect the costs of producing the goods and services. The system is built on the assumption that you, the consumer, have a dollar vote which you will cast in favor of those products you want and that in this way only those products that society wants will be produced. Several factors keep the system from working as we might wish.

Externalities. The first is what economists call spillovers or externalities. Nobody wants pollution, but pollution comes along with many of the things for which you spend money—*e.g.*, effluent from a paper mill, auto exhaust, or packaging disposal problems. Traditionally such costs have been left out of the cost-benefit equations. There are benefits that get neglected, too. How does one place a dollar value on a beautiful view, a clear stream, or a unique phenomenon like the Grand Canyon? Because such externalities have not been built into the equation, there has been little incentive to develop less-polluting alternatives and to protect resources whose value is mainly aesthetic.

A movement is afoot, as part of the environmental awakening, to begin assigning dollar-and-cents values to some of the externalities. Such devices as effluent charges and disposal taxes are attempts to induce businesses and individuals to reduce their contributions to pollution. The mere threat of imposing them, backed up by the general concern about pollution, has already caused some adjustments.

Some of the adjustments will mean the end of those consumer products and practices which do unavoidable and unacceptable violence to environmental quality. This, of course, is difficult when industries have grown up around unsound products (*e.g.*, a company whose sole product is DDT) or where "convenience" is involved. Just as the notions of cost and benefit must be broadened to include the externalities, so must the notion of convenience be reassessed. Is the convenience of non-returnable cans and bottles, plastic disposables, and highly toxic, nonselective household pesticides worth the inconvenience of solid waste disposal problems and threats to your health?

The Commons. A closely related problem has been described by Garrett Hardin in what he called the tragedy of the commons. In colonial New England the town common was the central pasture green whereon residents could tether their cattle. The common had a limited carrying capacity, and if it was exceeded, all of the cattle would suffer. Yet it was clearly to the individual farmer's advantage to have a cow, because he got essentially all of the benefit while the costs to the rest of the herd were split up among the other owners. This remained true even as the carrying capacity of the common was approached and exceeded. The tragedy of the commons describes what has happened to the air of Los Angeles, to the blue whales of the ocean, and to many other common resources. Each one of us, acting in his own self-interest, contributes to the common problem. The examples are endless: you take the car, not a bus; you buy that jaguar coat anyway.

Hardin goes on to disparage appeals to conscience as a solution to the problem. His alternative is mutual coercion mutually agreed upon. This is precisely what is beginning to happen today—government is trying to develop a system of mutually agreeable coercion by means of such devices as effluent charges and disposal taxes.

Garrett Hardin is correct. To the extent that this handbook merely helps individuals to assuage guilty consciences, it can never save us from tragedy. Action beyond the dollar vote is necessary. Hopefully, some of the ideas that follow will help you to see the need for such action.

Producer Sovereignty. John Kenneth Galbraith, in a recent newspaper article (Boston *Globe,* March 1, 1970), questioned the dollar vote assumption which, he pointed out, presumes consumer sovereignty. The illustrative example he chose was the transportation mess: "The cities are clogged with automobiles and have been extensively devoured by highways and freeways. Mass or commuter transit is slow, unreliable, uncomfortable, and filthy. If the consumer is sovereign, that, presumably, is the way he wants it; one sighs and knuckles under to the popular taste. But if the producer is sovereign and the automobile companies, as seems likely, are considerably more sovereign than most, we have here a reflection not of consumer but producer preference." Producer sovereignty is achieved in at least two ways, by advertising and by lobbying. Both are used extensively by the giant corporations, and both are essential targets for strong efforts to bring about some mutual coercion.

Hopefully, modern society is in transition from a cowboy economy to what has been termed a "spaceship Earth" economy. In the past few years the space program has dramatically illustrated to man how finite and precious the Earth's life-support system is. It has helped men to see how vital it is that resources be conserved and recycled. The challenge is survival. But hopefully, as we eliminate the diseconomies and social costs of our present system, we will achieve more than mere survival: we want to make Earth as appealing from the ground as it is from outer space.

On the personal level, this handbook seeks to demonstrate that there is an alternative to the consumptive rat race. In rational, palatable steps, you, the consumer, can modify your life style to bring it more into balance with your ecosystem. Here, too, the benefits to the individual go beyond self-preservation.

WHERE DOES THE MONEY GO?

In the United States, everything tends to be measured in relation to the gross national product. In economic terms, this is the sum of the market values of all goods and services that the nation produces in a given year. The average per capita share of the GNP is supposed to be a measure of the standard of living; however, the GNP includes all expenditures, productive and non-productive, and is uncorrected for social or environmental costs.

TABLE 1. THE GROWTH IN GROSS NATIONAL PRODUCT

	1940	1950	1960	1965	1967	1968*
Gross National Product (In billions of dollars)	99.7	284.8	503.7	684.9	789.7	860.6
Personal consumptive expenditures	70.8	191.0	325.2	432.8	492.2	533.8
Gross private domestic investment	13.1	54.1	74.8	108.1	114.3	127.7
Net exports of goods and services	1.7	1.8	4.0	6.9	4.8	2.0
Governmental purchases of goods and services	14.0	37.9	99.6	137.0	178.4	197.2
Population (In millions)	132.1	151.7	180.7	194.6	199.1	201.2
Per capita GNP (In dollars)	755	1,880	2,790	3,520	3,960	4,280

Source: *Statistical Abstract of the United States, 1969*   *Preliminary

One can see the growth in GNP, both in absolute and per capita figures. In real life terms, this is diminished by inflation and by whatever degradation of the environment costs (an externality). Note how much of the GNP consists of personal consumptive expenditures.

Personal consumptive expenditures are further broken down as follows:

TABLE 2. THE COLLECTIVE NATIONAL BUDGET FOR CONSUMER EXPENDITURES: 1967

	$ billion	per cent
Personal consumption expenditures	492.2	100.0
Durable goods	72.6	14.8
Nondurable goods	215.8	43.8
Services	203.8	41.4
Food and beverages	109.4	22.2
Alcoholic beverages	14.5	
Housing	70.9	14.4
Household operations	69.9	14.2
Electricity, fuel, and water	19.8	
Transportation	63.5	12.9
Cars	26.6	
Gasoline and oil	18.1	
Clothing, accessories and jewelery	50.7	10.3
Medical care	34.0	6.9
Recreation	30.6	6.2
Personal business	26.7	5.4
Life insurance	6.3	
Tobacco	9.2	1.9
Personal care	8.5	1.7
Religious and welfare activities	6.9	1.4
Foreign travel and other, net	4.0	0.8

Source: *Statistical Abstract of the United States, 1969*

Table 2 presents a rough estimate of the distribution of consumer spending, our collective personal budget. The magnitude of some of the items—cars, tobacco, alcohol, food, clothing, and shelter—testifies to the enormous markets that exist for individual consumer goods.

Table 3 indicates that the distribution of spending power in the United States is very uneven. The statement that the affluent American consumes a disproportionate share of the Earth's non-renewable resources and that he contributes much more to pollution problems than the ghetto dweller or the inhabitant of an underdeveloped nation has become trite, but it is true and very relevant. The buck has been passed far too much. Responsibility for halting environmental decay rests with the affluent, for they are the major consumers and, too, the managers of the system.

TABLE 3. DISTRIBUTION OF INCOME RECEIVED BY FAMILY UNITS: 1967

Income rank before taxes	Percent of total income	Lowest income (dollars)
Lowest tenth	1	......
Second tenth	3	1,860
Third tenth	5	3,175
Fourth tenth	6	4,627
Fifth tenth	8	6,000
Sixth tenth	9	7,441
Seventh tenth	11	8,800
Eighth tenth	13	10,350
Ninth tenth	16	12,270
Highest tenth	28	15,400

Source: *Statistical Abstract of the United States, 1969*

2. SHELTER

2. Shelter

WHERE YOU LIVE

Concern for the environment starts where you live. Items:

"The Federal Water Resources Council predicts that flood damage across the nation—now around $2 billion a year—will continue to increase despite flood-control programs and protective measures.

"Says Dr. Harold Thomas, research hydrologist of the U.S. Geological Survey: 'Despite past history and future projections, there is no ceasing of pressure to develop floodplains and other lands subject to water and flood hazards.'

"As open areas are taken over for suburban development, streets, sidewalks, parking lots, and buildings create an 'impervious cover' that prevents rain from filtering back into the soil.

"The northern Virginia suburbs of Washington, D.C. are typical examples of this, the experts say.

"There, new construction, including large shopping centers and parking lots, has eliminated 60 per cent of the natural drainage in some sections. Rainwater, which once soaked into fields and woodlands, now runs off very rapidly. The 'peak discharge'—or highest flow in the rivers and streams in the area—may be five times as great as before this urban growth took place."

—*U.S. News & World Report,* Dec. 15, 1969

■ In California, about 500 acres of open land falls prey to urban sprawl each day. The state, which has been a net exporter of food, is losing prime agricultural land

25

to the extent that she may soon become a net importer of food.

▪ In March 1970, the California State Water Resources Board put a freeze on all new building construction in several large areas around San Francisco until sewage systems are upgraded to handle the new loads. Cleveland and northern New Jersey have announced similar bans.

Land use

The reasons for rethinking our land use policies are compelling. Responding to the desires of millions of consumers, America has carved up millions of acres of land into small housing plots set in a sea of asphalt and concrete. This "suburbanization" has devoured prime agricultural lands and has filled in marshlands and estuarine areas that are vital anchor points for the ecological chains that support commercially important marine life. It has robbed urban dwellers of contact with natural open space and necessitated reliance on the private automobile for transportation, the latter a consequence with most disastrous implications for environmental quality.

Americans are a remarkably mobile people. Recent statistics indicate that about 19% of the total population moves in the course of a year. If you are planning to be this year's one out of five, consider carefully whether you want to pursue the private-home-in-the-suburbs aspect of the American dream. For there are alternatives.

Much recent interest, even at the federal level, has been shown in mobile homes. Mobile homes shipments have grown from 103,700 in 1960 to 121,520 in just the first four months of 1969. In 1969, 412,690 mobile homes, new and used, were sold, accounting for a reported 46% of the single-family dwelling sales for that year. They provide a less expensive alternative than new homes, whose median cost now exceeds $26,000. The trailer park, however, is hardly an attractive alternative even to Levittown, nor is the mobile home a real alternative in terms of land use to the land use problem.

Another development in the housing market has been

a move toward multiple dwelling units in new housing construction. About 43% of 1969's new dwelling units were in multiple occupancy buildings (three or more). The range of choice goes from skyscraper to cluster-zoned garden apartments, from ghetto public housing monstrosities to country club condominiums for the affluent. High-rise units and cluster apartments can be built at lower per-unit costs and they permit centralization of facilities such as laundries and refuse disposal and leave far more open space for public recreation and conservation uses. Such centralized housing also makes mass transit a much more feasible operation.

TABLE 4. COMPARISON OF LAND USE

conventional subdivision		cluster subdivision
32	Acres in streets	24
22,500	Linear feet of street	16,055
29	Percent of site in streets	19
80	Acres in building sites	41
590	Dwelling units	604
0	Acres of usable open space	51

Source: "Where Not to Build," *Technical Bulletin 1*, Department of the Interior

If you still decide that you are in the market for a private home, keep some of the following factors in mind:

■ Houses that are built on platforms carved out of hillsides or in the floodplains of rivers are more vulnerable to natural disaster.

■ Houses that are built in low areas or near water are more likely to have insect problems.

■ Most prime agricultural land and marshland have higher value to modern society as farms and as marshes than as housing subdivisions, even if their real estate dollar evaluation is high. Suitable alternative locations for the housing usually exist elsewhere; not so for the farms and marshes. Don't be a party to misuse of such land.

■ Open space in a congested area is valuable. If overall housing density must be increased, it should not be at the expense of necessary parks and open corridors. Again, to the extent that you can, stay away from improperly located housing.

■ Many older buildings can be made much more valuable by a relatively small investment in renovations. It is wasteful of resources to destroy structurally sound housing unless there is a very good reason to do so.

■ Find out whether a land use plan has been created for the area you want to live in. A properly constructed plan should indicate where housing, recreation, industry, business, and public facilities should go and is a protection against the irrational, haphazard development that has heretofore been the norm. If such a plan does not exist, work to get your area to hire landscape architects and planners to create one and then strive for its implementation.

■ Homes that have trees and grass surrounding them are likely to be cleaner, cooler, and quieter.

■ Some builders take greater pains to protect the valuable qualities of a building site (*e.g.,* trees, soil condition, proximity of neighboring buildings). Shop around before you select a builder; look at sample work in progress as well as finished products.

■ Find housing that enables you to get to and from work and shopping with minimum reliance on the private automobile. Locate near mass transit if you can. The tendency of the affluent to commute into the cities from their homes in the suburbs has meant congested highways, air pollution, wasted time and energy, and frayed nerves. At the same time, industry has been squeezed out of the inner cities; not infrequently, the inner city worker now has to commute *out* of the city to work!

These land use problems are knotty ones, and there is not much that you as an individual buyer or seller can do to influence trends. Your investment in a home or your monthly rent represents one of the largest components of your budget. You probably feel less free to make a totally rational decision for this reason. You should, however, keep in mind the fact that the decision on where you will live has a profound effect on how much money you will spend on other items, on what the environmental costs of the spending of that money might be, and on the quality of your life style.

Although land use patterns are the product of millions of consumer decisions, they are not really shaped by people acting as consumers. Rather, they are the result of people participating in zoning decisions, making investment choices as businessmen, voting on bond issues, and working through government to influence taxation policies.

Areas with potential geological instability or hazard

- Stay away from active fault zones.
- Avoid areas that are subject to periodic hazards such as floods, hurricane damage, and brush fires.
- Floodplains are, by definition, subject to periodic inundation, often every ten or fifteen years. A house should be more permanent than that. Also, beware of areas downstream from large water-storage floodplains that are under development pressure or unprotected.
- Ocean coastal areas are usually dynamic, that is, beaches are constantly being scoured away and the sand deposited elsewhere. Their ecology is also especially sensitive to abuse by man, and they are vulnerable to hurricanes and tidal waves.
- Steep slopes, especially those with poor ground cover, can be vulnerable to slumping and land- and mudslides.
- Sanitary landfills require many years, additions usually ten to twenty to settle before construction can be permitted.
- Construction on soft, water-saturated ground—on landfill in bays and on marshland, for instance—can be especially hazardous in earthquake zones.
- Subsidence of land due to mining and drilling operations is a severe problem in parts of the United States.

Sources of information on geological hazards. The U. S. Geological Survey and the Army Corps of Engineers are primary sources of information. You might also seek information from soil engineers, hydrologists, and civil engineers at local colleges. The Federal Housing Authority and the Veterans Administration do some evaluation of geological hazards before they guarantee loans, but, according to a recent report of a congressional committee, the FHA "has given inadequate consideration to the problems and hazards of areas with potential geologic instability, . . . has no program for training its technical personnel in geological problems, . . . and has not adopted a specific program for obtaining information . . . from Federal scientific and technical agencies." The VA "follows FHA requirements and procedures, such as they are, but neither seeks nor receives information as to past FHA rejection actions."

> Natural, ocean-facing dunes of windblown sand, so vulnerable to wave erosion during times of severe storms, yet so essential for the protection of the island's interior [Fire Island, New York], have become the most highly prized parcels of real estate. Hundreds of summer homes, including many expensive ones, have occupied these protective dunes. In many places these homes, with their spindly supportive legs, now stand exposed to the full fury of storm-driven waves. Senseless tampering with protective dunes has made many of the island's interior communities susceptible to an invasion by the sea. Much is at stake, both in terms of personal financial investments—now totaling several tens of millions of dollars—and the stability of the island itself.
> —*Natural History Magazine,* June–July, 1970

SECOND HOMES AND VACATION COTTAGES

For a long time there has been a group of people, admittedly a minority, who get a lot out of camping and roughing it in the wilderness, away from people and civilization. On the base of their conservation movement, the recent environmental awakening has grown. What has become clear is that the fight to save wilderness is also a fight to protect civilization, for both are threatened by the same problems. Although the movement has broadened, the conservationists find that they still have to fight for wilderness. Their motto has become "In wildness is the preservation of the world."

As Americans have become more affluent, greater numbers of them have sought to escape their deteriorating urban and suburban environments, to join the traditional conservationists in experiencing some of the joys of the natural world. They travel great distances and flood the state and national parks and seashores to more than capacity. The need for more such recreational facilities is pressing because of the limited carrying capacity that natural ecosystems have. Overuse becomes consumption.

While only 2.9% of Americans have second homes, about 57% of these, some 874,000 in 1967, were vacation cottages. The growth in such housing has been great. The problem is that the development pressure has been greatest on the seashores and in the mountains, especially near ski areas, where the nature of the land resource is most sensitive to development. Fortunately, large areas of wildness are semi-preserved by national forest status. Unfortunately, relatively little coastline is protected, and the absolute protection of a network of natural preserves under the Wilderness and Wild Rivers Acts is far from complete.

The tragedy of carrying the system of private, piecemeal ownership of tracts of land to the remaining natural areas of this country may not be obvious to those who merely want a piece of it for themselves. Think of this before you invest in resort developments that threaten California's Point Reyes and Lake Tahoe, the Florida Everglades, the barrier islands of the Eastern seaboard, the Minnesota backwoods, and other areas of outstanding wilderness value.

From Cape Cod, Mass., to Point Reyes, Calif., members of national seashore supervisory staffs report overcrowding, lack of facilities, littering, and erosion by man and nature as threatening large sections of the 600-odd miles of Federally controlled coastal recreation preserves on ocean and bay front.

At the same time the few shoreline areas still available are being snapped up for industrial and private development at a record-breaking rate.

—*New York Times,* May 31, 1970

DESIGN OF THE HOME

It shouldn't come as a surprise to anyone with an awareness of ecology that the elements that go into a successful housing design are many and that they all relate one to another. Thus, the site, choice of materials, and design are properly coordinated so that the final product is esthetically pleasing, economic to build, and to maintain. It takes talent and training to carry out the design of housing as it should be. It is unfortunate that very little of the talent that is available has been used to design housing for the general public. Monotonous acres of uniform, prefabricated suburbs and monolithic towers of public housing in cities are testimony to our non-concern.

If the private builder of a home has enough money, he can hire the experts to build him a home that relates well to its environment. He should be cautioned, however, against the tendency to extravagance. Luxury can be obtained without robbing the public of valuable resources (e.g. sites that should remain undeveloped, extensive use of such materials as redwood) or imposing large burdens on public utilities (e.g. heavy use of power and water or large burdens on public sewer systems).

No one should embark on the project of building a home without careful thought and planning. If and when you undertake such a project, keep in mind some of the environmental factors that are discussed below.

Most of us will never build a home of our own. Everyone, however, exerts control to some degree over his shelter and the way in which it relates to the broader community interest. We remodel, we plant, we dig, we landscape, we maintain or we don't maintain, we deal with pests—and we buy large numbers of products that have impact on the quality of the environment that we and others experience.

What follows looks selectively at some of the above-mentioned decisions.

What should your house be made of?

> The choice for the people of America is either for more recreation, more parks, or more wilderness, or whether they want houses to live in and forest products to use in daily living.
>
> We can have no more wilderness if we are to provide houses for the American people.
>
> —Timber industry lobbyists,
> Sierra Club *Bulletin,* May, 1969

The above statements were attributed to timber industry lobbyists in early 1969, at the start of the battle over the Timber Supply Act. These men were working for passage of a bill that called for the harvesting, in 15 years, of timber that, under sustained yield, would be taken over a hundred-year period. The statements were, of course, extreme. One year later, lumber prices were down, largely because of a very slow housing market.

It does take lumber to build houses, and it takes more to build some than others. If everyone's home were built with redwood paneling inside and redwood siding outside, there would be little chance of saving even the small portion of virgin redwood forest that has been preserved today. In a very real sense, the virgin California coastal redwood is an endangered species. As such it deserves the protection of a consumer boycott until the magnificent redwood cathedrals are adequately protected.

There are, of course, many alternatives to the use of

lumber in housing construction. Prestressed concrete, metals, cinderblocks, bricks and other materials compete with lumber. Plastics are used more and more in building construction. In plumbing, floor covering, insulation, paneling and other uses where permanence is a virtue, wellmade plastics have a definite place. Especially interesting to environmentalists is the growing list of building materials that are made from industrial byproducts that were formerly thrown away or incinerated.

■ Boise Cascade makes a particleboard out of wood chips and sawdust.

■ Calcium sulfate from spent pickling liquor in the steel industry and from inorganic sludges in the pulp, paper, and fertilizer industries can be made into gypsum wallboard.

■ Fly ash from power industry furnaces has found markets in precast and structural concrete and building blocks and stands ready to take over from clay in face brick manufacture.

MAINTAINING YOUR HOME

Your home represents a major investment. It makes sense, practically and ecologically, to take good care of it.

The exterior. Keep the exterior of the house in good shape. Design and construction play a big part. Walls, ledges, and the roof should be designed to shed water, and crawl spaces should be ventilated so that dampness does not cause wood to rot. Gutters must be kept clear, especially in the winter when ice can force its way up under roofing tile. Siding and trim should be kept properly painted.

Termites. Termites are a problem in some areas of the United States. They are social insects that live in colonies in the soil. Because they commute, as it were, to their meals, the best precautions to take involve keeping a healthy distance between the soil and the wood parts of your house. Ideally, there should be no cracks or empty spaces in the foundation through which they can pass, and the area under the house should be ventilated. (Termites need moisture.) Termite control is one area where careful use of pesticides can be justified, but it doesn't make sense to use these hazardous chemicals without also taking the above precautions. Chlordane or lindane (not aldrin or dieldrin) can be used to treat the subsoil under and around the foundation, and construction timbers that have been pressure-impregnated with creosote can be used. To deal with an invasion, call in a reputable pest control operator and ask him to explain exactly what he is doing.

Plumbing. Plumbing problems, like most maintenance problems, are best handled preventively. Clogged drains present the most common problem. Obviously, the first principle is not to throw anything down the drain that shouldn't go there. Plumbing outfits say that their biggest money-makers are stuck sanitary napkins and disposable diapers. Use only as much toilet paper as you need, and avoid washing food scraps and other waste down the drain.

There is a wide variety of chemical products available to clear drains—Drāno, Liquid Plumr, and Plunge among them. These products contain some very caustic chemicals that present serious hazards to user and non-user alike. Never use them with casual abandon, as most people do. Ecologically, they have the undesirable effect of adding to the burden of harmful chemicals in the water supply. They should *not* be used regularly. The two exceptions to the rule are baking or washing soda and yeast tablets which are sometimes added to help out a septic tank.

Most drain problems can be dealt with mechanically, *i.e.*, by non-polluting methods. The plunger is the most time-honored tool. Any boy scout with a home repairs merit badge should be able to clear a clogged sink trap (the S-shaped pipe under your sink). Plumbers have mechanical devices, such as the Roto-Rooter, that enable them to dig out tough plugs in inaccessible locations. Note that prior use of a chemical drain cleaner can present a hazard to the plumber.

Root invasion of drainpipes can be an expensive problem. If you have a blockage of the main drain and suspect root problems, call in a plumber. He can clear the block temporarily with a Roto-Rooter or a similar device and then locate the problem area. It is wise to deal with a root invasion promptly, before extensive excavation and replacement of large sections of drain become necessary. Once again, a chemical solution to the problem is not recommended. Chemical root killers flush rapidly by the target area and pass on to damage nontarget plants elsewhere.

Keep the location of drainpipes and septic tanks in mind when you plant trees and shrubs. An ounce of prevention . . .

If you have a septic tank, don't use disposable diapers. Garbage disposal units also put an especially large burden on a septic tank; dish- and clothes-washers are less of one. In your septic tank, anaerobic (*i.e.,* they don't need oxygen) bacteria degrade wastes. Most of the volume percolates off into the subsoil (which must be porous), leaving behind a sludge that must be emptied every few years. If this is not done, the soil absorption system gets clogged up and can be restored only by being rebuilt—an expensive proposition. Foul-smelling overflow from a damaged septic tank can be traced by a dye test. See your local Department of Public Health.

Keep your faucets in good repair. Replacing the gasket is a simple matter that can save a considerable amount of wasted water.

Heating your home

Heating and cooling equipment uses a large proportion of the energy that flows into your home. Peak power demand almost always comes on the coldest and the hottest days. Homeowners face a wide range of heating conditions and an equally wide choice of equipment. Normally the choice is made wholly on the basis of dollar costs. But what are some of the environmental factors?

Heating efficiency. The job of most heating systems is

to convert the energy that is stored chemically in fuels into heat. Thus, when you compare electricity with gas and oil, the starting point is always the fuel and the end point heat in your home. Because the various fuels burn with different outputs of heat, normal practice is to start with BTU's (British thermal units, the amount of heat needed to raise the temperature of one pound of water one degree Fahrenheit) of fuel energy.

Electric heating involves converting the heat content of the fuel into electrical energy, transmission to your home by wires, and conversion back to heat in a furnace or heat pump. The first step is usually done with an efficiency of only about 35%, and sometimes a lot less. That is, commonly 10,000 to 11,000 BTU's of fuel are burned to produce 1 KWH (kilowatt hour) of electricity. If the process were 100% efficient, it would take only 3413 BTU. The balance is waste heat. Transmission and distribution losses vary; in a fairly compact urban area they are about 7%. Thus, though conversion of electric energy to heat in the home is 100% efficient, the overall process is only about 30% efficient, or less.

Actually there are two types of electric heating. Resistance heaters work by running the electricity through a resistor that gives off heat at 100% efficiency. Heat pumps can achieve more than 100% efficiency because they pull in heat from the outdoors and add it to the resistance heat which their motor produces. This advantage is lost when the outdoor temperature drops much below 40° F.

If the fuel is burned in a furnace in the home, energy conversion to useful heat is much higher.

Type of Furnace	Efficiency
Stoker–fired coal	60% to 75%
Gas– and oil–fired	
Boiler	70% to 80%
Atomizing burner with forced air	80%
Oil–fired with pot–type burner	70%

Thus, less fuel energy reaches the atmosphere as waste heat and unburned fuel. Waste heat is no problem. The greater efficiency of oil and gas heat over electric heat is not offset by the energy costs of distributing the fuel.

Pollution and heating. All power pollutes. (See p. 84.) Electric heat is not clean heat if you take into account the greater thermal pollution, the lower efficiency and consequent greater use of fuel, the gases that are discharged to the atmosphere from power plant stacks, the radiation pollution from nuclear power, and the drowned rivers and valleys that lie behind hydroelectric dams. Fossil fuels, too, must be won from the ground and transported, and that means mines and wells and oil spills.

Exactly how you balance these environmental costs in your choice of a home heating system is a rather subjective matter. Which pollution is worse? Local factors and the type of fuel can be relevant. For example, natural gas has relatively low sulfur content. If you live in an area with high levels of SO_2 air pollution, you should use gas or low–sulfur oil. In such a situation, electric heat might make sense, provided the power plant was located in another area, where air pollution was not a problem, and that the plant's pollution was well controlled. The technology that is being developed to clean up stack gases can be economically applied to large utilities, but not to the small home heating unit.

Regardless of how you heat your home, you can reduce the adverse impact of your heating system on environmental quality. At the same time, you will save on heating costs.

■ Keep your equipment in good operating condition. In this way you can improve efficiency and reduce unburned fuel to a minimum.

■ Air filters in a forced–air system should be replaced periodically so that they remain unclogged.

■ Keep the flue and chimney in good shape to reduce the risk of gases escaping into your house.

■ Dirt on radiators can reduce transfer of heat to the room air.

■ Reduce your heating requirements by properly insulating your home, especially the ceilings and outside walls. Over the long run, it's an excellent investment.

■ Use storm windows; large windows should be double glass.

■ Caulk and weatherstrip joints.

■ Take advantage of the sun. Windows with a southern exposure pick up the sun's warmth. During the summer, they can be shaded by awnings if they are not shaded by trees.

■ Trees also help to shield the house from winter winds.

■ Regulate the heat in each room at the radiator, air vent, or the electric unit. If you can't and you need to warm up a cold area, use a small heater rather than overheat the rest of the house.

■ If during the cold months you don't use a room, don't heat it.

■ If donning a sweater or adding a blanket to the bed at night is comfortable, lower the thermostat by a degree or two. Raising the setting only one degree costs 3% to 4% more in fuel consumption; raising it five degrees, 15% to 20% more.

■ Turn the heat down at night and during the day if the house is empty. A timer control that does this automatically can be installed.

■ The special rates (and gold medallions) that electric companies offer to entice you to go "all electric" don't make their power any less polluting.

Cooling your home

It used to be that electric utilities experienced their heaviest power demand on the darkest, coldest day of the year. With the advent of the air conditioner, the peak now comes on the hottest day instead. Air conditioners use a lot of power. Water–cooled models also use a lot of water—75 to 150 gallons per hour for each 12,000 BTU of cooling capacity. (Consult page 102 for more information about room air conditioners.)

In naturally hot climates, people long ago devised the

afternoon siesta as a natural and non–polluting way to beat the heat. In a modern, fast–paced world, however, this would not do. Men must work through the day from 9 to 5 in cities that are naturally five to ten degrees hotter than the suburbs anyhow—in buildings that are totally closed to the outside atmosphere. In such a system there isn't much of an alternative to air conditioning, despite its enormous energy and water costs.

In the home, hopefully, you can find less polluting ways to find comfort despite the heat. The following are some suggestions.

■ A well insulated house will stay cooler.

■ A home can be made cooler by installing awnings over the windows to keep direct sunlight out.

■ Those rooms with northerly exposures tend to be cooler, as do basement rooms. Center your activities there.

■ Trees provide shade, and moderate the heat. If you can arrange it, move your housework out of doors, into the shade of a tree. If you don't have a tree and have a place to plant one, do so.

■ Large paved areas next to the house will absorb and reflect the sun's heat into the house.

■ As long as the house is cooler than outdoors, keep the shades drawn and the windows closed.

■ Electric appliances produce considerable waste heat. Keep appliances and lights off.

■ When it is cooler outside than in, drawing air into the house is wise. This is best done by finding the direction of natural ventilation in the house. Place a fan in front of the window that naturally exits the air and let the fan assist the hot air out.

■ Fans are rated in cubic feet per minute (c.f.m.). The recommendation is usually that fan capacity be enough to change the air in the space you are cooling once every one to three minutes. A room 12′ x 12′ x 8′ would need a fan rated at 384 to 1152 c.f.m. to meet this standard.

■ In attics, where temperatures commonly soar out of

sight, it is frequently wise to install an attic fan to moderate the temperature there.

■ In very dry climates, evaporating water can have the effect of cooling the air.

■ Leaving the refrigerator door open will not cool down a room, unless the waste heat from the refrigerator motor is vented to the outside in some way.

■ If you own an air conditioner, use it sensibly. Don't leave it on when you are not at home. Air condition only as much space as you need. Also, supplement the efforts of your machine with some of the steps outlined above.

■ Heat pumps, mentioned earlier as heaters, can be reversed to act as air conditioners. Like air conditioners, they are expensive to buy and to operate.

3. THE LAND AROUND YOUR SHELTER

3. The Land Around Your Shelter

ELEMENTS OF LANDSCAPING

Fences aren't required

Imagine what would happen in your neighborhood if the fences came down—the posts and boards and chain link that divide suburban open space into tiny back yards, the hedges that mark off the boundaries of each family's domain. Something like the re-creation of the commons (see p. 19) could happen, each family donating some of its sovereign territory to the neighborhood and each receiving more in return. There could be broad open places where children could run and play, and communication from neighbor to neighbor and even between neighbors several times removed might blossom.

This is suggested as a practical alternative to fences and hedges. In some situations it makes very good sense. Have you ever considered it, or discussed it with your neighbors?

It is also suggested to illustrate the value of broadening your perceptions of the environment that surrounds the shelter that you call home. The "typical American back yard"—an enclosed plot of ground with a stall for the car, a barbecue pit or brazier, a swing, aluminum chairs, some asphalt and plot of grass with sprinkler—creates an environment that is too often empty of any natural beauty and a horizon that inhibits communication and perception of a broader community.

Drainage: Where does the water go?

Rainwater can be viewed in either of two ways: (1) as a pollutant that is best ushered off the property into the nearest drain as directly as possible, or (2) as a beneficial —indeed, necessary—resource that should be induced to stick around. The second school of thought is ecologically more sound. The asphalt and concrete approach to landscaping prevents rainwater from seeping into the earth to replenish the groundwater supply, shunting it instead into sewer systems that simply cannot be built large enough to handle the quick runoff from a storm. The environmental costs are returned to you in the form of taxes for expanded sewer systems, if they don't come in the form of a flooded basement. Asphalt and concrete also have the disadvantage of being good reflectors of noise and heat.

The factors that control the absorption of water into the ground include the ratio of natural land to asphalt-covered land, the contour of the land, the amount of ground cover, and the condition of the soil. A few general considerations are relevant to a broad variety of conditions:

■ Devices such as gutters and drainpipes tend to concentrate water. This is fine if there is a reason for it such as shielding a walkway from dripping or collecting water for a cistern. But the practice is too often merely a holdover from the get-it-down-the-drain school of thought. Once the water is concentrated, it should be spread out again to percolate into the ground. Run the water out of the gutter onto a splash block, onto gravel, or into a more elaborate French drain. There are exceptions. If you happen to live on a site where lubrication of the subsoil can cause landslides, percolation of water into the soil should be discouraged and good drainage encouraged.

■ The combination of inadequate ground cover and steep slopes has caused extensive problems, especially in Southern California. The potential for land erosion in some sites is obvious and they should be avoided.

■ Soil that is porous will absorb and store water more

efficiently than clay soils will. Clay soils, often encountered by new home owners, must be reworked to make them fertile and thus porous; no amount of chemical fertilizer can make soil productive if it won't hold water. You can rework your soil by using a variety of materials that are readily available—slag, well-crushed glass bottles, sawdust and wood chips, leaves, manure, sewage sludge, composted garbage, and even shredded paper. All additionally share the virtue of being reused "waste."

Thank a green plant

Trees and other plants are great moderators. They soak up sound, break up the wind, and create cool shade. In a real sense, they are a non-polluting alternative to acoustic tile and air conditioning. Their roots absorb and hold moisture, while their leaves give it off. Their branches provide a home for birds and their fruit and seeds provide food for both men and animals.

Trees and green plants also participate in the biochemical cycle in which carbon dioxide and sunlight combine to make carbohydrates and oxygen. This chemical reaction is central to the whole fabric of life on this planet, for it produces almost all of our energy. There is a romantic notion that planting trees measurably increases the amount of oxygen we have to breathe, and that killing all green plants and the green algae and phytoplankton of the sea would bring about the suffocation of man. Scientifically, this argument is not backed up by the facts. Plants consume the same amount of oxygen when they decay or are eaten as they produce while growing. Furthermore, based on what we know of fossil fuel reserves and the stocks of hydrocarbons stored in living plants and animals, all of these could be burned without reducing the oxygen content of the atmosphere by one percent. Oxygen comprises 20% of the atmosphere.

A problem does exist, however, with carbon dioxide, which makes up less than one percent of the atmosphere. There is great concern that increasing the concentration of carbon dioxide in the atmosphere can have considerable effects on the climate. The "green-house effect" tends to increase the temperature here on earth by trapping solar radiation. CO_2 levels are up 15% since 1890 and are expected to be 30% higher than now by 2000. The reduction of the total amount of vegetation on the earth does raise CO_2 levels; the burning of fossil fuels, however, is far more significant.

But hold on! Trees shouldn't need chemists to justify their existence.

Plant a live Christmas tree

Each year millions of pine trees are cut down (killed) to provide festive decoration for the holiday that celebrates the birth of Christ. The yearly quest for the perfect Christmas tree usually produces a less-than-perfect specimen, chopped down several weeks earlier in the north country and ready to drop its needles and become a fire hazard in short order.

There is an attractive alternative to dead Christmas trees. A modest-sized pine can be bought live and kept for several years in a tub of sufficient size. You should consult with a local nursery about the proper choice and care. Each year it can be brought indoors for a week or two during the Christmas season, and when it grows too large, it can be planted on one's own property or donated to the municipal parks department.

Think before you plant

Growing anything, especially in the city and suburbs, requires at least a little forethought. If you are creating a landscaping scheme for your home, trees and shrubs should be selected with scale and proportion in mind. They should be placed to create shade and to be shaded as needed. One also should keep soil conditions and, in urban and industrial areas, air pollution in mind. To get complete, accurate information that is relevant to your situation, contact a local nursery, garden club, or landscape architect.

Keep both aesthetics and ecology in mind. Design diversity into your scheme, for diversity is what helps to stabilize natural systems. It is also important that the species you choose be able to thrive, for healthy plants resist pests and weak ones attract them. You can plant to attract birds and squirrels or to keep them away, bearing in mind that birds help to control insects.

The trees can't breathe the air

Virtually all principal types of plant crops have suffered economic damage from air pollution. Among these are citrus in California and Florida; grapes and orchids in California; peaches in Utah; tobacco in the East; and timber—especially pine—in the East, the West, and Canada. Because of pollution damage it will be increasingly difficult to grow truck crops, particularly leafy ones like lettuce and spinach, near large cities.

—*The Yearbook of Agriculture*, 1968

A thousand acres of towering ponderosa pines in the San Bernadino Mountains, fatally afflicted by smog from nearby Los Angeles, were turned over by the United States Forest Service today to a lumber company for commercial logging.

—*New York Times*, April 2, 1970

Working with Zinfandel grape vines, [researchers find] that the average vine produces a mere 6.9 pounds of grapes when it grows in an ambient (smoggy) environment compared to 17.8 pounds when the vines get clean air. In addition, smog stunts the growth of the vines and results in grapes that are smaller and less sweet.

—*Chemical & Engineering News*, June 8, 1970

The damage to vegetation caused by air pollution affects everyone, either directly or indirectly. Attention is being given to the breeding of resistant strains of sensitive species, but this takes a long time. As Table 5 shows, some plants possess a sensitivity to specific pollutants while others have a general sensitivity. Admittedly sketchy and incomplete, the table is offered with the reservation that more effort should be spent on learning how we can end pollution and less on how to live with it.

TABLE 5. POLLUTION-SENSITIVE AND RESISTANT PLANTS

Trees generally considered especially sensitive

Dogwood	White pine
Redbud	Ponderosa pine

Trees generally considered resistant

Quaking aspen	Red oak
Cottonwood	English oak
Little-leaf linden	Pin oak
Weeping willow	Norway maple
Washington hawthorn	
Ailanthus (Chinese tree of heaven)	
Ginkgo (Sensitive to auto exhaust)	

Flowers and shrubs

Lilac (ozone, generally Sensitive)
Petunias (PAN S)*
Carnations (ethylene S)
Orchids (ethylene S, an indicator)
Snapdragons (ethylene S)
Geranium (ozone R)
Gladiolus (ozone R)
Pansies (PAN R)

Vegetables and other crops

Spinach (ozone S)
Tomatoes (ozone, ethylene S, an ethylene indicator)
Potatoes (ozone S, SO_2 R)
Romaine lettuce (PAN S)
Beans (SO_2 S)
Pinto beans (ozone, PAN S)
Beets and chard (generally S)
Onions and celery (SO_2 R)
Corn (SO_2, PAN R)
Peppers (ozone R)
Cabbage (PAN R)
Mint (ozone R)
Alfalfa and barley (SO_2 S)
Cotton (SO_2 S, ethylene R)
Wheat (SO_2 S, PAN R)
Tobacco (ozone S, an indicator)
Bluegrass (PAN S)

Notes: *PAN is a photochemical product of ozone, nitrogen dioxide, and hydrocarbons that is present in smog.
S = sensitive; R = resistant.

SPECIAL PROBLEMS

Salting walkways and roads

A variety of inorganic salts are used in northern climates to keep streets and walkways free of ice. The salts are rough on the undersides of cars and on footwear, floors, and wherever they are tracked, unless they are washed off promptly. Environmentally, the practice has become very damaging. The salts are leached into the soil and water supply, weakening the resistance of plant life to pest invasions and—notably in several New England towns—contaminating the municipal water supply.

There are several alternatives to salt. Cinders, available from steel plants and other places, can be used. Sand is nonpolluting, more effective at lower temperatures, and can be recovered and used again. And, of course, the snow can be removed before ice forms.

4. GARDENING: WEEDS AND PESTS

4. Gardening: Weeds and Pests

It would be impossible to cover adequately in these few pages either of the topics of this chapter—pesticides or gardening. For this reason, you are advised to consult the bibliography in appendix one (I) for more information.

In the section on pesticides it has not been assumed that all pesticides should be banned. Most responsible experts do not take this position. However, no pesticide should be considered absolutely safe and no pesticide should be used casually. If you follow the suggestions made below, you will probably find that using pesticides is often inconvenient. If you don't follow them, it will definitely be dangerous.

Pest control and organic gardening should both start from the same point—an understanding of the pests, the plants, and the soil. Once you have a proper appreciation of the way nature handles things, you will probably conclude that her ways are best.

Because gardening is the closest that most people get to dealing directly with natural ecosystems, it is important that gardeners have some understanding of how natural ecosystems work.

The essential fact to bear in mind is that natural ecosystems are balanced and generally self-controlling. Each plant, insect, and animal has its niche and coexists with

55

the rest of the system. The ecological balance is maintained by a variety of mechanisms, some of them as simple as one species feeding on another, and others as subtle as insect sexual attractants and natural, plant–derived insecticides. Most living things are controlled either by predators, by limitations on the supply of an essential factor in their diet, or by competition with other members of the system for living space. In nature there are few omnivores; few all-purpose pests.

PESTICIDES ARE NOT THE ANSWER

The individual who wants to keep a garden, or even just a few trees, shrubs, and a lawn, has been led to believe that such an endeavor must be plotted out as a war would be waged. The enemy is the pest—weed or insect—and the arsenal contains a battery of insecticides, fungicides, miticides, nematicides, and herbicides. The phobia against pests has been carefully cultivated.

Instead of dealing with pest problems intelligently, one is conditioned to reach for the spray at the first sign of an "invasion" or even, in the absence of any problem, as a "preventative" measure. The agents that are used are not designed to deal with specific pests. Instead they are broadly toxic biocides that wipe out whole systems of plants and insects, the bad ones and the beneficial ones (*e.g.*, bees and lady bugs) as well. A housekeeper wishing to avoid damaging himself and his environment should keep the following in mind:

■ Eradication of a pest is generally not a necessary or even a desirable goal. Most "pests" are important to some other member of the ecosystem, in many cases to one considered "desirable."

■ Eradication of the pest is usually not attainable, partly because of contamination from non-eradicated areas, and partly because many of the target pests develop a genetic resistance to the pesticide.

■ Use of pesticides tends to become addictive. Nonselective chemicals destroy the natural controls, making it easier for the pests to stage a comeback. This leads to more frequent and heavier doses. This speeds the development of resistance so that new (and generally poorly tested) pesticides must be introduced to maintain control. An area so treated can become entirely sterile, and such addiction quickly becomes more expensive than relying on natural controls or putting up with minor pest damage.

> BACKFIRE!! "When parathion was applied to a cole crop the number of predaceous and parasitic species were reduced by 95 percent whereas the number of plant-feeding species were reduced by only 8 percent. Following this type of disruption, population outbreaks of the plant feeders occur. Because the parasitic and predaceous species are absent, the plant feeding species increase explosively."
> —*Mrak Commission Report*, p. 207.

▪ To get away from frequent "fixes" the chemical-spray addict tends to rely on long-lived chemicals which retain their toxicity for years. Such persistent pesticides are transported by air or water and thus are now found on virtually every part of the Earth's surface. They concentrate in the bodies of living things, and inevitably they reach you through the air you breathe, the water you drink, and the food you eat.

▪ Few pesticides have been developed so far that are very selective, *i.e.*, toxic only to a specific pest and not to other creatures in the ecosystem. To develop selective pesticides is uneconomical for the manufacturers.

▪ As our knowledge about them grows, more and more pesticides appear to pose serious threats to human health.

Now we will look into some of the available methods of pest control—both those that do and those that do not employ nonselective pesticides.

Weeds

A plant is not a weed until someone decides to call it one. According to one definition, a weed is simply a plant in the wrong place. Ecologists tell us that weeds tend to be problems only in ecosystems that have been disturbed, that is, they tend to get crowded out in a "climax" (ecologically stable) system.

Unfortunately, man creates subclimax communities all the time—for instance, when he wipes out a natural control, disturbs a natural ecosystem by excavation, or creates a monoculture (concentration of a single plant). Agriculture is an excellent example of the last situation. There man tries to trade increased yield of a particular crop in exchange for decreased stability.

The lesson for the home gardener is that he can minimize weed problems by creating a healthy environment for the plants he wants. This is especially true for ground covers like lawns and ivy beds. In the case of row crops or flower gardens, however, it is desirable to keep the areas between plants free of any vegetation, and this creates an ecologically unstable situation that can be maintained only by artificial means.

The traditional method has always been cultivation—the hoe and the tractor-drawn cultivator. Modern farmers, however, have turned to herbicides (weedkillers) because the expense is lower—but not the environmental costs. The primary domestic application of herbicides has been to control lawn weeds, but they are also used for general gardening purposes.

Before even considering the use of chemical herbicides for the home garden, however, you should try safer methods of weed control. Most home gardens are small enough to make manual weeding a reasonable proposition. Your attitude is important: if digging in the garden is recreation, then weeding will not be much of a chore. If you can keep the soil well tilled and weed regularly, the "problem" will be minor.

Another approach is mulching. Mulch is a layer of material that is placed on the surface of the soil to conserve moisture and inhibit weeds. It has the added advantage of reducing work and of benefitting the soil since it eventually decays and is dug in. Mulching is a must for any serious gardener. The material used can be straw, grass clippings, sawdust, sea weed, cotton-gin trash, peanut shells, or other natural organic materials. Some people advocate mulching with plastic films, paper, and even aluminum foil, but the wisdom of using such non-biodegradable materials is doubtful. Another method is stone mulching, using flagstone-sized rocks to fill in between rows. Mulching is an art. The choice of the proper mulch and the timing of its application are refinements that delight the organic gardener.

Herbicides. Weedkillers are best avoided entirely by the home gardener. This is the advice of a large number of the experts. Their advice, however, contrasts sharply with that found in the manufacturers' ads, which tell us that herbicides are a safe and convenient way to deal with weeds.

Weedkillers have been shown to have damaging effects on living things, including man, so it doesn't make sense to assume a given product is safe. Consumer and expert alike must have the answers to a rather large number of questions before a well-informed decision about herbicide use can be made.

Some of the questions are:

- What active ingredients does the product contain?
- What else does it contain that might affect the action of the active ingredient (synergistic effects)?
- Are there any contaminants that could be dangerous?
- Does the product break down into anything that is harmful?
- How long does the herbicide persist in the environment?
- How readily is it transported away from the target area?

- Does it concentrate in particular organisms or localities?
- Does it do the job that it is supposed to do?
- How does it affect non–target organisms?
- What are the short-term effects? Is it acutely toxic?
- What are the longterm effects?
  Does it cause cancer (carcinogenicity)?
  Does it cause birth defects (teratogenicity)?
  Does it cause mutations (mutagenicity)?
- Can the product be applied safely?
- Is the product packaged safely?
- Are the label warnings adequate?
- Do we know enough about it to regard it as safe?

Where are the answers to these questions? Information has been gathered on many of them, but it is woefully incomplete and inconclusive in most respects. The nature of the problem is such that a definite conclusion that a product *is* safe is not possible; there is always the possibility that some effect has been missed. The evidence is always negative—that a product is *not* safe.

Another problem is that most of the experiments have been done with mice and other lab animals, and there is a good deal of uncertainty in the extrapolation of the results to man. Scientists are reluctant to experiment on men, but manufacturers, on the other hand, are experimenting daily with all of us. Their "experiments" are not controlled and it is difficult to sort out the effects. The last question, then, is the critical one. Do we know enough about these products to regard them as safe?

Unfortunately, the two parties who should be in a position to provide a reasonable answer are the manufacturers and the government. The story of their failure to protect the health and welfare of the public in this matter has been dealt with by others. In part, the problem seems to be that the government has tended to apply the judicial doctrine, innocent until proven guilty, to DDT, 2,4,5–T and who knows what else. The problem is compounded by the slowness with which a product is taken off the market, once the government decides to move.

Recent actions taken on DDT and the herbicide 2,4,5, –T illustrate this. Following a decade of effort to bring about a ban on DDT and related long-lived ("hard") pesticides, the government announced, in November, 1969, a phased *cancellation* of some DDT uses starting with all uses for shade tree pests, pests near water bodies, house and garden pests, and tobacco pests. The word cancellation is misleading because this action can be (and is being) appealed, during which time interstate shipment of the pesticide is permitted to continue. The decision to *suspend* use of liquid formulations of 2,4,5–T around the home and in lakes, ponds, and irrigation ditches which was announced in April, 1970 was actually a much stronger move. Suspension halts interstate shipment of the product and cannot be circumvented during an appeal. Neither "ban," however, was total in any sense. "Essential" uses of DDT (unspecified) may continue; DDT's relatives remain unregulated; and solid formulations of 2,4,5–T (most are) will continue to be sold. Furthermore, stocks of products containing DDT and 2,4,5–T will continue to be sold as long as they last. Thus, government regulation doesn't permit you—the consumer—to relax your vigilance.

Improper and Proper (?) Uses. The message here is that herbicides are hazardous and that there are viable alternatives for most home uses. Assuming that this is the most ecologically sound viewpoint to adopt, take a look at your own use of herbicides. Weigh the environmental costs and try to see how you can minimize them.

How do you apply herbicides? You may be using them and not know it. Many lawn fertilizers contain herbicides to control crab grass and lawn weeds. If the fertilizer does its job, the herbicide should not be necessary. Hazard can arise from lawn conditioners that use 2,4–D and 2,4,5–T in granular form. In hot weather they can vaporize into the atmosphere and affect plants a fair distance away.

You can also cause damage to your neighbor's lawn, and he can cause damage to yours, by spray application and subsequent drift of the mist. Application of herbicides from an aerosol can or by means of garden hose attachments invites this sort of contamination. Use of hoses has the additional hazard that a drop in water pressure could cause some of the pesticide to siphon back into the hose, possibly contaminating your whole water supply.

Weed bars (herbicides in a wax bar) are another approach to herbicide application. These are used for spot control, either rubbed directly on the target plant or left next to it. In the latter case they are a hazard to any child or animal that comes upon one. Dragging the weed bar behind the lawn mower is also suggested by the manufacturers. This could be especially bad if, by accident, the mower managed to get hold of the bar.

In general, broadcast application of herbicides is most unwise; however, spot application to cracks in pavement or to problem plants like poison ivy using granules in a shaker, weed bars, or liquids in a spray or aerosol can is effective and can be relatively safe. The proper herbicide should be selected and applied to the most vulnerable parts of individual plants.

Consult pages 65–66 for a list of suggestions for reading pesticide labels and of precautions that should be observed whenever a pesticide is used.

Which herbicide? The reader who wants a list of most of the commercial herbicides available should consult the ratings presented in the June 1970 issue of *Consumer Reports*. This study included 174 chemical weedkillers and considered safety both to the user and to the environment. Only one out of four products was considered suitable for use by home gardeners; 38 were rejected because they lacked the USDA registration number, others because they bore the "DANGER" and "WARNING" labels. Those containing 2,4,5–T, paraquat, arsenites, and methanearsonates were judged to be too toxic. Those containing dicamba, simazine, and erbon were considered too persistent.

The "acceptable" weedkillers were placed in three categories. Pre-emergent weedkillers, which are applied before the weed seeds germinate, were considered to be "the only class of herbicides that may be safe for use near vegetable plots, near fruit trees, on flower plots and lawns, and near ornamental trees and shrubs" and "the only recommended way for the home gardener to control crabgrass chemically." The active ingredients considered safe for use included *DCPA, trifluralin, ambien, diphenamid, EPTC,* and *siduron.*

The post–emergent weedkillers are members of a class of herbicides that came out of war-related research on plant hormones. They are effective on growing broadleaf plants but are also "toxic enough to damage any but wellestablished lawns." *Consumer Reports* further advises that "none should be used anywhere but on the lawn," and points out that "to choose the right herbicide for a particular weed, you must be sure of the weed's identity (a bother you can forget if you just uproot the weed)." *2,4–D* and *Silvex* (also known as 2,4,5–TP) were judged "acceptable." It is interesting to note, however, that tests have indicated that several esters of 2,4–D have "potentially dangerous" teratogenic (fetus-deforming) effects. About 79 million pounds of 2,4–D were produced in 1968, most of it used on corn and wheat and some on lawns.

The third class of herbicides, the nonselective weedkillers, wipes out virtually all growing vegetation and should be used only for spot treatment unless it is scorched Earth you desire. Classed as "acceptable" in this group are *petroleum distillates, amitrole, AMS,* and *dalapon.* It should be noted that amitrole, the herbicide that caused the cranberry scare of Thanksgiving 1959, is known to cause cancer in animals and is now suspected of being a teratogen as well.

Because of the hazards that even "approved" herbicides present, *Consumer Reports* advises that "children and pregnant women should be kept away from lawns and garden treated with herbicide until a good rain or a watering lowers the hazard to some extent."

TABLE 6. NAMES OF SOME COMMON PESTICIDES AND HERBICIDES

PESTICIDES sometimes hide behind their longer formal chemical names. This list should help you to identify common pesticides when they appear in mysterious garb on pesticide labels.

The chlorinated hydrocarbons: Finding the fragment "chloro-" in the pesticide name doesn't necessarily mean that it belongs to the family of infamous persistent chlorinated hydrocarbon pesticides which are listed here:

aldrin: 1,2,3,4,10,10-hexachloro-1,4,4a,5,8,8a-hexahydro-1,4-endo,exo-5,8-dimethanonaphthalene

chlordane: 1,2,3,4,5,6,7,8-octachloro-2,3,3a,4,7,7a-hexahydro-4,7-methano-indane

DDD (TDE): 2,2-bis(p-chlorophenyl)-1,1-dichloroethane

DDT: 2,2-bis(p-chlorophenyl)-1,1,1-trichloroethane, dichloro diphenyl trichloroethane, chlorophenoethane, Genitox*, Anofex*

dieldrin: 1,2,3,4,10,10-hexachloro-6,7-epoxy-1,4,4a,5,6,7,8,8a-octahydro-1,4-endo,exo-5,8-dimethanonaphthalene

endrin: 1,2,3,4,10,10-hexachloro-6,7-epoxy-1,4,4a,5,6,7,8,8a-octahydro-1,4-endo,endo-5,8-dimethanonaphthalene

heptachlor: 1,4,5,6,7,8,8-heptachloro-3a,4,7,7a-tetrahydro-4,7-methanoin-dene

benzenehexachloride (BHC): 1,2,3,4,5,6-hexachlorocyclohexane

lindane: the gamma isomer of BHC

toxaphene: chlorinated camphene containing 67–69% chlorine

methoxychlor: 2,2-bis(p-methoxyphenyl)-1,1,1-trichloroethane

THE PHENOXY HERBICIDES:

2,4-D: 2,4-dichlorophenoxyacetic acid (also salts and esters of this compound), Verton*D, WEEDAR*, DMA-4*

2,4,5-T: 2,4,5-trichlorophenoxyacetic acid

2,4,5-TP: Silvex

OTHER INSECTICIDES:

Malathion: O,O-dimethyl dithiophosphate of diethyl mercaptosuccinate

Parathion: O,O-diethyl-O-p-nitrophenyl phosphorothioate, Phoskil*, Thiophos*, Folidol, E-605,.Niran*

Sevin: carbaryl or 1-naphthyl N-methylcarbamate

Vapona: dichlorovos or 2,2-dichlorovinyl dimethyl phosphate, DDVP, Herkol*, Dedevap*

OTHER HERBICIDES:

Amitrole: aminotriazole

Dalapon: 2,2-dichloropropionic acid or Dowpon*

Dicamba: 3,6-dichloro-o-anisic acid or Banvel

Diphenamid: N,N-dimethyl-2,2-diphenylamide or Dymid*

Simazine: 2-chloro-4,6-bis(ethylamine)-5-triazine, Princep*, Gesapum*, Amizine*, Primatol S*

Trifluralin: α,α,α-trifluoro-2,6-dinitro-N,N-dipropyl-p-toluidine or Treflan

Reading a label

There is no excuse for not carefully reading the label, and this includes all of the fine print. This should be done before you purchase the product.

■ Look for the Department of Agriculture (USDA) registration number. A product lacking this may not even meet the safety standards set forth in the present, rather inadequate, Federal regulations.

■ Look for the following warnings. "DANGER, POISON," with skull and crossbones, meaning fatal in very small doses. "WARNING" means very toxic; small amounts can kill a child. "CAUTION" means moderately toxic. These warnings on the label refer to acute toxicity—the short-term effects, not the longterm ones. "DANGER" and "WARNING" means that the pesticides are too dangerous for routine home use.

■ Sort out the advertising claims from the warnings. This is frequently easy—the claims are printed in large type: PREVENTS CRABGRASS; KILLS BUGS DEAD; CLEAN, PLEASANT ODOR!; NONTOXIC TO HUMANS AND PETS; while the warnings are relegated to small type: Keep out of reach of children; Avoid inhalation; Avoid contact with skin; Toxic to fish and wildlife. It is not uncommon to find contradictory claims and warnings on the same package. Let common sense and caution be your guide when it comes to following instructions for use. There isn't enough room on most packages for adequate instructions, and those provided are, in fact, often misleading and dangerous, especially the illustrations that accompany them.

■ Look carefully at the statement of ingredients. Learn which components are known to be dangerous, which are suspect, and which are believed to be safe. It is wise to avoid combinations of pesticides—for example, insecticides in herbicides or fertilizers with either insecticides or herbicides in them.

Precautions that aren't on the label

■ Take care to fit the pesticide to the pest. Don't use the right pesticide at the wrong time. Don't use a persistent pesticide when a short-lived one will do.

■ Avoid treatments that will damage beneficial insect populations, especially insect predators and pollinators.

■ Use no more than you need. An overly heavy application can damage the plant you wish to protect and adds to the risk of undesirable effects.

■ Buy only as much as you need. If you must store it, keep it out from the reach of children, locked up if possible.

■ Thoroughly wash out any containers you use for mixing, and be careful with the wash water. Store the pesticide in its original container, for the label contains important information.

■ Keep pesticides away from the water supply.

■ Avoid inhaling pesticide vapors. In general, no pesticide should be used in such a manner that it will contaminate the air.

■ Wear gloves and trousers to protect your skin. If you get some on you wash it off immediately, for it can be absorbed through the skin. Change your clothes and bathe after using any pesticide.

■ Disposal of empty containers and excess pesticides is a major problem. Burial 18 inches deep in your back yard is not a proper solution. Nor should any pesticide ever be dumped down a drain. Check with your state department of public health or natural resources. In some areas, private groups (*e.g.,* the Massachusetts Audubon Society) have set up programs to accept unwanted pesticides. Although incineration is a good way to dispose of persistent pesticides, you should *never* try to do this yourself—the fumes can be very dangerous.

Pesticides

The situation with the other pesticides—insecticides, miticides, nematocides, fungicides, and rodenticides—is similar to that with herbicides, except that many of the other pesticides are more persistent and less selective. The advice regarding the reading of labels and the precautions to be taken during use remain the same in any case.

The chlorinated hydrocarbons—DDT, Aldrin, Chlordane, BHC (benzene hexachloride and lindane), DDD (TDE), Dieldrin, Endrin, Heptachlor, Methoxychlor, and Toxaphene—are notorious for their persistence. Despite their growing unpopularity, they are still very much with us, even on retail shelves. Their replacements have been organic phosphates and carbamates. These tend to be less persistent, which is an advantage; however, non-persistence in itself does not mean they are harmless, as some advertising might indicate. The organic phosphates, in fact, include the most toxic of the pesticides, such as TEPP and Parathion, which are also nonselective.

Some pesticide resumes. The following pesticides have been recommended by several authorities as being "acceptable" for careful and restricted use. While they may be the pesticides of choice, it should be clear that they are no substitute for the non-polluting pest control measures mentioned later.

■ *Pyrethrum.*—A natural insecticide that does not persist and is essentially non-toxic to warm-blooded animals. Fish are more susceptible. There are, however, many cases of humans developing a strong allergy to pyrethrum. Often combined with the synergist, piperonyl butoxide. (*Allethrin* is a synthetic analogue)

■ *Rotenone.*—An insecticide which is naturally produced by some plants. Low toxicity and apparently no carcinogenicity. Poisonous to pigs and fish.

■ *Ryania and sabadilla.*—Also naturally derived insecticides. Apparently "safe."

■ *Nicotine sulfate.*—Highly toxic but not persistent.

■ *Carbaryl* (Sevin, 1-naphthyl N-methylcarbamate) —Relatively non-persistent and said to be harmless to wildlife. Widely used. Recent evidence indicates that Sevin is teratogenic (fetus-deforming).

■ *Methoxychlor* (2,2-bis-)p-methoxyphenyl)-1,1,1-trichloroethane)—Significantly less toxic than its sister chlorinated hydrocarbons. Persistent but apparently can be metabolized by living organisms. Lethal to fish but apparently doesn't cause serious damage if properly used.

■ *Malathion* (O,O-dimethyl dithiophosphate of diethyl mercaptosuccinate)—Relatively non-toxic for an organic phosphate. Severe kills of birds and fish have resulted from indiscriminate use. Especially rough on bees.

■ *Diazinon.*—A nonselective, reasonably short-lived phosphate. Toxic to birds and fish.

■ *Abate.*—A larvicide that is used for mosquito control but that doesn't kill the adults. Generally considered safe around small mammals, birds and even young rainbow trout, but it is toxic to shrimp and may kill other crustaceans.

■ *Baytex.*—An organic phosphate that disappears fast. However, a concentrated dose kills birds almost on contact. Will kill bees and shorebirds at the doses recommended for mosquito control.

■ *Dessicants.*—These kill insects by drying them out on contact, penetrating their waxy exoskeletons. Nontoxic to humans and pets. They include Dri-Die (silicagel), Drione (with pyrethrum), and Perma-Guard (diatomaceous earth).

■ *Milky spore disease.*—A bacterial insecticide specific for Japanese beetle grubs.

■ *"Bacillus thuringiensis."*—A bacterial insecticide specific for a variety of species of moths and certain other Lepidoptera.

■ *Bordeaux mixture.*—A fungicide and insecticide consisting of a mixture of copper sulfate-calcium hydroxide. Avoid mixtures fortified with lead or calcium arsenate.

■ *Warfarin.*—A rodenticide that, on repeated exposure, acts as an anticoagulant. Will kill rats and mice. Presumably a child which ate it all at once would only get sick.

TABLE 7. CHEMICAL CONTROL OF PESTS

THE PROBLEM	"RECOMMENDED*" CHEMICAL CONTROL
Ants	In woodwork—dessicant powders In lawns—chlordane (minimal)
Aphids	Wash them off; good biological controls available; nicotine sulfate, pyrethrum, rotenone, malathion.
Bedbugs, cockroaches, fleas, silverfish	Dessicants; malathion, Diazonin
Caterpillars	Rotenone, Diazonin, methoxychlor, carbaryl Sevin
Chiggers	Malathion
Chinch bugs	Diazinon, Sevin
Cutworms	Diazinon, Sevin
Earwigs	Dessicants; chlordane for very difficult areas
Flies	In the house—fly paper or a fly swatter
Grasshoppers	Diazinon, Sevin
Gypsy moth	An overrated pest; use Sevin
Japanese beetles	Grubs—milky spore disease Adults—malathion, Sevin

Lawn moths	Diazinon, Sevin
Leafhoppers, leaf miners, leaf rollers	Diazinon
Mice, rats	Mousetraps; Warfarin
Mites (red spiders)	Oil spray, hot water
Mosquitoes	Larvae—pyrethrins, oil
	Adults—abate, Dibrom, malathion
Scale insects	Diazinon, malathion, Sevin
Spittlebugs	Malathion, Sevin
Termites	Chlordane
Thrips	Nicotine sulfate, Diazinon, malathion, rotenone
Wasps, hornets	Rotenone in the evening
Wireworms	Diazinon
Wood borers	Diazinon

Note: *The "recommended" chemical control is not always the most desirable control. Where so-called cultural control (e.g. eliminating breeding sites) or biological controls are available, they are generally greatly preferable.

Source: This table is based on a similar one prepared by the National Audubon Society.

Dangerous herbicides and pesticides. Here are a few of the pesticides that one should avoid at all costs; this list is by no means exhaustive.

■ Piperonyl butoxide—Actually not a pesticide but rather a synergist. Its use permits lower doses of the pesticide that it accompanies by rendering it more toxic. Also exerts its synergistic effect when it might not be desired. Known to interfere with detoxification of 3,4-benzpyrene, a carcinogen. Synergistic with Freon, the common aerosol propellant, in inducing liver tumors in mice. Is used in a lot of "safe" insecticide formulations, but . . .

■ Arsenic in any form—Used in insecticides, rodenticides, and herbicides. A cumulative poison in animals and soil. Can render soil permanently sterile. Carcinogenic.

■ Mercury (organic and inorganic)—Widely used as a fungicide to preserve seeds and on golf courses. Wildlife eat treated seed and become unsafe for human consumption. Several instances of human poisoning via this route. Mercury of industrial origin has contaminated many of our waterways.

■ The persistent hydrocarbons (DDT, aldrin, BHC,

lindane, DDD, dieldrin, endrin, heptachlor, toxaphene)—
DDT is notorious. The others should be notorious too.
Two members of the group, chlordane and methoxychlor,
are sometimes recommended (see table 7) but should
never be used casually.

TABLE 8. PESTICIDE AND HERBICIDE PRODUCTS TO WATCH
OUT FOR

Avoid lawn products that combine herbicides with fertilizers:
  Scotts Turf Builder plus 2 (2,4-D) and Halts Plus
Avoid products that contain extremely toxic or persistent chemicals:
  Shell, Raid, and Black Leaf Ant and Roach Killers contain dieldrin.
  Real-Kill Bug Killer in a "new bug gun" that "makes bug killing
    fun!" contains dieldrin.
  Arsenic is contained in crab grass killers by Black Leaf, Eveready,
    and Breck.
  Scotts haze rose care (powder) contains 5% DDT.
  Antrol Multi-purpose Rose Spray and Black Flag Wasp & Hornet
    Killer contain lindane.
  Vigoro Fungicide for Turf and Dichondra contains methylmercury
    dicyanamide
*Any product bearing a DANGER, POISON or WARNING on the label
is too toxic for home use.*
Be wary of products that promise long-lasting action:
  Shell No-Pest Strips contain Vapona (DDVP) imbedded in wax.
    As the wax evaporates, the Vapona is released. In hot, humid
    weather the release can be rapid enough to deliver more than the
    designed dose. You and your food are exposed over long periods
    of time to the same concentration of this nerve gas that the bugs
    are. It kills them.
Watch out for pesticides in the following products:
  Shelf paper impregnated with chlordane and lindane. Because
    tolerances for these pesticides in food have not been set, USDA
    and FDA have had trouble banning the treated paper.
  Dry cleaning fluids with some types of mothproofing.
  Swimming pool chemicals.
  Furnace filters.
  Paints.
*Stay away from applicators that pose unacceptable risks to the user or
his environment:*
  Burgess Vibrocrafters' Insect Fogger (120 volts, 8 amps for $20)
    says on the box: "Fogged areas may be occupied immediately, but
    the insect-killing effects remain for hours." Their Special Insect
    Fog Insecticide contains 1% malathion. Good luck!
  The Bernz-o-matic Super Jet Fogger ($35) is propane powered and
    is similarly advertised. The packaging encourages you to use it
    for picnics, fishing, camping, and barbecues. Don't breathe deeply.

Specific pest problems

A few examples will indicate the way an environmentally responsible housekeeper or gardener deals with a
pest problem.

Leaf-chewing insects. The following advice comes from the Massachusetts Audubon Society: "Much of the pesticide use in back yards is for the control of defoliating caterpillars on ornamental trees and shrubs. The caterpillars are a nuisance, and the damaged leaves temporarily disfigure the yard. But, if untreated, the outbreaks are short-lived. The caterpillar population is limited by parasites and predators, and the trees or shrubs survive unless they are already old and weakened. On the other hand, if pesticides are used, the natural enemies are reduced even more effectively than the caterpillars, the first outbreak is often followed by more serious ones, and each calls for heavier spraying.

"Defoliating insects are as much a part of nature as the trees. They are the food of birds and other animals whose breeding season is timed to take advantage of the insects' annual appearance. When the trees are sprayed, the birds and other caterpillar-eaters are eliminated, and the yard is less attractive throughout the year."

Dutch elm disease. Dutch elm disease is the result of a fungus. Most control programs are aimed at the European bark beetle which spreads the fungus. The method of control least damaging to the environment combines cutting down and removal of infected trees with careful pruning of noninfected trees, for the beetle requires dead elm wood to breed. Elms that are close to one another are especially vulnerable to spread of the disease; a solitary tree is safer.

Age, elimination of groundwater by pavement, air pollution, salt from winter roads, and herbicides can weaken an elm and make it more vulnerable. Heavy spraying has been the common approach to controlling the beetle. Now that DDT has been prohibited for that purpose, the shift is to methoxychlor, which is as effective against the beetle as DDT was. While DDT may have saved some elms, it did so at the expense of the robin population by poisoning earthworms.

Mosquitoes. Only strong pesticides that are hazardous to other forms of wildlife will kill adult mosquitoes, thus the only rational control methods are those aimed at

mosquito breeding grounds—termed "source abatement."
Culex, the most common household variety of mosquito,
lays its eggs in any container that holds a little stagnant
water—rain-filled pails and toys left outdoors, bird baths,
old tires, blocked-up gutters and downspouts, and catch
basins that don't drain—so it helps to eliminate any sources
of stagnant water. You can facilitate drainage by digging
drainage ditches; however, it is important not to overdo
the drainage bit to the extent that important wildlife
habitats are destroyed. If it is a local canal, lake, or pond
that is the source of the mosquitoes, try stocking the
water with fish. Massachusetts Audubon reports that min-
nows, goldfish, bluegills, and bass will gobble up the
larvae.

Another preventive approach recognizes that mosquitoes congregate in certain areas, such as the low-lying
flood plains near rivers. For this and other reasons, such
areas are not appropriate sites for homes.

If the ounce of prevention has not worked, make use
of other non-polluting defenses against mosquitoes. Keep
your screens in good repair and, where appropriate, use
mosquito netting. A bottle of rub-on mosquito repellant
is preferable to sprays. One can also purchase "black
light" electrocution devices which attract and then zap
mosquitoes on contact. (e.g., Bug-a-Boo Insect Lantern,
45 watts for $9 and the Chadwick-Miller Electronic Insect
Killer, 50 watts for $7.)

Slugs and snails. Slugs and snails appear to have a
fatal taste for beer. A shallow pan of beer, fresh or stale,
placed near an infested ivy patch will lure hundreds of
them to a drunken death by drowning.

Crabgrass. The best approach to crabgrass problems
in your lawn is to encourage growth of the desirable grass.
Crabgrass and good lawn grasses need different conditions
to thrive. A healthy, thick lawn turf will crowd out crabgrass and other broad-leaf weeds. The good grass is
favored by a fertile topsoil that is deep and rich in humus.
Thus, if you are planting a new lawn, build a soil that is
rich in organic matter and properly fertilized before you
plant your lawn. If you wish to rescue an existing lawn,

the soil can be built up by spreading organic materials on your lawn in installments so as to avoid smothering it. Peat moss, shredded compost, and leaf mold are good builders. Any lawn that is growing also needs to be fed periodically. Phosphate rock, potash, lime, bone meal, dried blood, and soybean meal are good natural fertilizers. To know what your soil needs, a soil test is advisable. See page 78.

A hard-packed lawn must be aerated to let air and moisture into the roots. Good grass tends to be deep-rooted, whereas crabgrass is shallow-rooted. Thus, it is wise to administer an occasional heavy drenching to your lawn rather than a frequent light watering. Wait until the lawn is so dry it just shows footprints and then give it one or two inches of water (measured by putting a container under the sprinkler).

Because crabgrass grows close to the ground, you can also favor the good grass by setting the height of your mower at two to four inches. Cutting frequently enough so that you never have to clip off more than one third of the total grass length at a single mowing is advisable.

Crabgrass propagates from season to season through seeds. Sweeping up the lawn clippings with a sweeper when the crabgrass is seeding can therefore be helpful. It is also wise to start a new lawn in the fall so that the grass has a head start on crabgrass and weeds in the spring.

Weed control in a new lawn is best done without resorting to herbicides. Have a little patience and encourage the lawn by using the methods described. If your lawn is small enough, hand weeding will suffice while the new lawn takes over and prevents new weeds from getting established.

Pest protection by companion planting

Many plants possess natural pesticides. This is true of the onion-garlic family, the aster family, most strong-smelling herbs, and many others which are commonly considered weeds. By interplanting these with unprotected species, you can protect your garden from pests without resorting to harmful synthetic pesticides. This is a simple matter in most home gardens. Many of the protective plants are attractive perennials, useful in their own right. Specifically:

■ Marigolds act against a wide variety of grubs, larvae, and nematodes in the soil without harming the beneficial earthworm. Organic farmers advise interplanting them with tomatoes, eggplants, peppers, strawberries, and beans to protect the latter from nematodes (small parasitic worms that feed off plant roots). (Pyrethrum, a commonly used insecticide, is derived from chrysanthemums, marigolds, and other members of the aster family.)

■ Asparagus also repels nematodes. Planting tomatoes in an asparagus patch is mutually beneficial, since the tomato repels the asparagus beetle.

■ Green beans similarly protect the potato from the Colorado potato beetle while the potato protects the beans from the Mexican bean beetle.

■ Garlic, onions, and chives provide protection against aphids. For instance, chives can be planted in a rose garden and garlic and onions can be planted around the bases of peach trees.

■ Onions and garlic also have bacteriocidal and fungicidal properties.

■ Sage and mint protect cabbages, broccoli, cauliflower, kohlrabi, and Brussels sprouts. Basil protects tomatoes. Savory protects beans.

■ Spearmint, julep mint, and tansy repel ants, and basil and mint are supposed to repel flies. Certainly a sprig of mint is more attractive than an aerosol bomb.

■ Mustard acts as a trap plant for cabbage; the cabbage-eating harlequin bug prefers the mustard.

■ The fruit of the Osage orange tree reportedly will rid a room of roaches.

■ Grinding up plants that seem to be resistant to a pest and making a slurry with water creates a concoction that many say works quite well as a pesticide spray. Elderberry leaves are a favorite for this practice.

The following list of suppliers of pest–repellant herbs is taken from the May 1970 issue of *Organic Gardening and Farming*.

Nichols Garden Nursery
Pacific North
Albany, Oregon 97321

Greene Herb Gardens
Greene, R. I. 02872

Meadowbrook Herb Garden
Wyoming, R. I. 02898

Casa Yerba
P.O. Box 176
Tustin, Calif. 92680

Snow-Line Farm
Rt. 1, Box 270
Yucaipa, Calif. 92399

Pine Hills Herb Farms
P. O. Box 144
Roswell, Georgia 30075

Geo. Park Seed Co.
Greenwood, S.C. 29646

Other organic practices

In addition to companion planting, organic farmers control pests by clearing away or plowing under plants that have produced their crop before they become prey to pests in their old age. They have also found that it is unwise to plant certain crops together (*e.g.*, tomatoes and corn, because they share a common pest) or to put the same plants in the same location from year to year.

There is also a host of techniques for trapping pests, preventing them from reaching their target plants (for instance with paper collars that fit around the stem of the plant), and bolstering the resistance of target plants that are better described in a book on organic gardening.

Natural controls

Hopefully natural controls will provide the means of controlling pests in the future. As scientists gain a better understanding of how natural controls operate, we should depend less and less on the chemical pesticides that have proven so destructive. Some of these methods are usable right now.

Not all species of the same plant have the same *resistance* to disease and pests. Today's plant and seed catalogues are fatter than those of several years ago largely because of the progress that has been made in breeding resistant species, even of trees. When consulting catalogues, keep your eye out for such terms as "immune" and "susceptible."

Another promising technique is the use of *natural predators.* The desirability of frogs and birds is well known. The beneficial effects of such insects as ladybugs, ladybeetles, wasps, dragonflies, damselflies, aphid lions (lacewing larvae), and praying mantises are usually ignored due to the common phobia about bugs. But it is important that the distinction between good and bad insects—and also that between beneficial and harmful bacteria and fungi—be made.

The beneficial insects are already being made commercially available. For example, ladybugs can be bought at a cost of $6.50 per gallon, delivered. The gallon contains about 75,000 bugs. At 40 to 50 aphids eaten a day, that is a lot of aphids. Some Kansas farmers found that they were able to control an outbreak of greenbugs on a crop with 258 gallons of ladybugs at a cost of about 75¢ per acre versus $2.50 per acre for chemical control. The ladybugs have the additional advantage that they stay around only as long as the pest does.

The following list of suppliers of natural predators is based largely on a list in the July 1970 issue of *Organic Gardening and Farming*.

Ladybugs   Bio-Control Company
                              Route 2, Box 2397
                              Auburn, Calif. 95603

                              L. E. Schnoor
                              Rough & Ready, Calif. 95975

Lady bird beetles   World Garden Products*

* Advertised in the *New York Times,* 6-21-70.

	Insect Control Center Department 6-21T 2 First St. E. Norwalk, Conn. 06880
Praying Mantises	Eastern Biological Con. Co. Rt. 5, Box 379 Jackson, N.J. 08527
	Gothard, Inc. P. O. Box 332 Canutillo, Texas 79835
	Robert Robbins 424 N. Courtland East Stroudsburg, Pa. 18301
Trichogramma wasps (Trik-O)	Gothard, Inc. P. O. Box 370 Canutillo, Texas 79835
Trichogramma wasps and Lacewings (Aphid lions)	Vitova-Insectary, Inc. P. O. Box 475 Vitova, Calif. 92376
Milky Spore Disease (Doom)	Fairfax Biological Laboratory Clinton Corners, N.Y. 12514
Bacillus thuringi- ensis Disease (Thuricide)	International Mineral & Chemical Crop Aid Products Dept. 5401 Old Orchard Rd. Skokie, Ill. 60076
(Biotrol)	Thompson-Hayward Chem. Co. P. O. Box 2383 Kansas City, Kansas 66110

Note: The reader is referred to the article in *Organic Gardening and Farming* and to the manufacturers for more information.

There are other methods being developed that offer advantages over the presently available methods of pest control. Some of them will probably be used only by the professional exterminator, but others will become commercially available. Insect juvenile hormones can be used in infinitesimal amounts to prevent insects from maturing into adult pests. Insect sex attractants can be used to lure pests into traps where they can be readily killed. Another approach involves sterilizing male insects in large numbers by irradiation and releasing them to mate with the wild females, a technique already used with considerable success. Recent research indicates that it may be possible to breed the sterile males.

THE SOIL

The importance of the structure and fertility of the soil with regard to water runoff and the ability of plants to withstand the challenge of pests has been mentioned. A proper soil does not cake, contains a large amount of organic matter, is not too acidic or alkaline, and has a sufficient supply of all the necessary nutrients. The soil that you have to work with probably falls short of the ideal in a number of respects. To find out what your soil needs, a soil test is recommended. You can buy kits that test for humus, nitrogen (N), phosphorus (P), potash (K) and pH (acidity) at garden stores. Sudbury Laboratory of Sudbury, Mass. 01776 has kits that range in price from $6 to $40. Or you can take your sample to a state experimental station. The sample should be representative of the top six inches of your soil.

Fertilizing

Although a soil test is advisable, it isn't absolutely necessary, for you can be pretty sure you are headed in the proper direction if you put lots of organic material into the ground. As a plant grows it draws nutrients from the soil and the air, and when the plant is harvested, these nutrients get taken away. Unless the soil is replenished, it quickly becomes less fertile.

Organic fertilizers, then, have the advantage of closing the ecological loop. Unlike inorganic fertilizers, they also boost the humus content of the soil. A wide variety of materials serve admirably as fertilizers. Do you throw away weeds, grass clippings, leaves, kitchen garbage, or sawdust? With simple composting and mulching techniques these and, for that matter, essentially anything organic can be made into useful soil builders. The challenge to the thrifty gardener is to locate fertilizers and compost materials that would otherwise be waste. With little effort it is easy to fertilize at less cost than with the less effective chemical fertilizers. You can make use of animal manure, wood ashes, dried blood and bone meal or tankage from slaughterhouses, spoiled hay, hulls and shells, cottonseed, seaweed, seashells, and sewage sludge. Some municipal sewage plants give away their activated sludge; some mix it with leaves. Milwaukee has, since 1928, marketed the treated sludge from its plant as Milorganite.

Most commercial fertilizers bear an analysis such as 5-10-5. The numbers stand for the percentages, respectively, of nitorgen, phosphorus, and potash or NPK. The references on organic gardening found at the end of this chapter present similar information for the natural fertilizers.

Composting

Natural compost is both an excellent fertilizer and a convenient way to recycle wastes back into the soil where they belong. While the official, super-duper, 14-day compost pile is a rather large-scale operation, the gardener can prepare compost in his backyard quite easily on a smaller scale. The basic idea is to let soil bacteria and earthworms decompose the organic material; no special innoculation of bacteria is needed. Shredding the material is helpful. It is wise to use a variety of materials, not just leaves or garbage, to build your pile. Adding manure, bone meal, ground limestone, and phosphate rock will assist the decomposition process. Air is another essential ingredient; the pile should have ventilation and should be turned periodically.

Composting materials can be buried in a trench or the composting can take place in a specially constructed box, a garbage can with vents, or just in a pile. Pets and other scavengers can be discouraged by a lid or by covering the pile with some dirt.

Innovation is the most useful tool for both finding composting materials and processing them. To an alert gardener a tree-pruning crew means mulch and the rotary lawnmower serves as a shredder.

MINIGARDENS

You don't have to own a large spread to do some gardening. The tiniest plot of ground, as long as it gets some sunlight, will yield bountifully under proper care. The image of the carefully spaced row garden should not confine your plans. Some of the most productive gardens are found in poor countries where the garbage dump is farmed. The plants find fertile soil there and don't care whether they are in regular rows. In fact, the irregular arrangement interjects some ecological diversity that makes these gardens less susceptable to pests.

Gardening can even take place in a window box or a flower pot. A U.S. Department of Agriculture pamphlet entitled "Minigardens for Vegetables" has a lot of good ideas along this line.

5. CONSUMING ENERGY IN THE HOME

5. Consuming Energy in the Home

WHY BE CONCERNED ABOUT ENERGY?

Throughout the one hundred and seventy years since Thomas Malthus proposed that the geometric growth of the world's population was bound, someday, to outstrip the capacity of the Earth to feed that population, the debate over his proposition has raged. Although the question of how many people the world can feed is far from resolved, the general consensus seems to be that constraints other than lack of food will probably limit the population first, at least in many parts of the world. This theory is certainly being borne out in the United States. It isn't hunger so much as the deterioration of our air and water that has indicated to us that we are bumping up against some of those Malthusian limits.

The reaction of some people has been to attribute all of our environmental ills to "too many people," yet the fact is that most of the problems are growing much faster than our population is. There is a growing awareness that the problems are in large part due to our standard of living. The purpose of this chapter is to illustrate the connection between our standard of living and pollution by examining the energy-consumption problem in the U.S.

Why concentrate on energy? Because here the connection is especially clear. Many of the biggest polluters—oil companies, electric utilities, strip miners—are really energy companys, for they sell energy in the form of gas, gasoline, oil, electricity, and coal.

What do higher levels of power consumption mean?

- More blowouts like those in Santa Barbara and Louisiana.
- More Torrey Canyon–type oil spills.
- More acid mine drainage.
- More strip mining.
- More black lung disease for miners.
- More valleys drowned behind hydroelectric dams.
- More SO_2 in the air from fossil fuel plants.
- More radioactive wastes to dispose of.
- More hazards from nuclear power plants.
- More pump storage facilities for peaking power.
- More unsightly distribution lines.
- More waste heat to thermally pollute our rivers.

This is what production of power has meant in the past.

What are the chances of providing customers with nonpolluting energy in the future? It is true that sulfur can be stripped from fuels before they are burned, or from stack gases before they are emitted. The risk of a blowout or a spill can be reduced. Distribution lines can be placed underground. Strip mines can be reclaimed and plant sites "beautified." However, while risks can be minimized, they can never be eliminated. As long as more oil wells must be drilled and more oil must be moved on the seas, more oil will be spilled. Furthermore, the energy industry has met increased demand by scaling up its operations and by adopting new technologies such as nuclear power. Thus, the consequences of a miscalculation are becoming more disastrous.

In addition, there will continue to be competition for land and water resources. Hydrolectric potential is realized at the cost of flooded valleys and free-flowing rivers. Extraction of fuel will continue to destroy land values. Thermal power plants, either fossil-fuel or nuclear, produce waste heat. By 1980 they are expected to use one sixth of the average daily water runoff for cooling, and by the year 2000 one half of the available water and even more during the summer months. Burning fuels, too, adds to the burden of CO_2 in the atmosphere.

Is nuclear power the solution? Some would have you believe so; however, projections indicate that nuclear power will fill only 25% of demand by 1980. Growth in nuclear capacity has actually lagged behind predictions, largely because of technical problems and the growing awareness that nuclear power is not pollution free.

Other advances in technology lie over the horizon. Nuclear breeder reactors are expected to come along in time to prevent a shortage of reactor fuel. They may also help reduce heat loads slightly. Tamed nuclear fusion is pie–in–the–sky for right now, and the problems with radioactive byproducts that might accompany it are unclear. Less dramatic advances, such as magnetohydrodynamics (MHD) and electrogasdynamics (EGD), may also reduce thermal pollution somewhat by improving efficiency. Thermoelectric generators, solar batteries, and fuel cells are available now, but their costs are prohibitive. For example, solar cells may eventually get down to $100,000 per kilowatt of generating capacity versus $100 per kilowatt with a steam power plant. Only fuel cells are likely to become competitive with present methods of generating power.

An energy crunch. That's how energy experts sized up the present situation in the U.S. at the North American Fuel Technology Conference at the University of Ottawa. . . . Electrical power generation is the most immediate critical problem. Even as conferees assembled in Ottawa, warnings of brownouts and blackouts began to appear. The problem stems from heavy growth in energy consumption. . . . There is no easy way out of the energy problem.
—*Chemical & Engineering News,* March 23, 1970

Projected heat rejection from energy use [in the year 2000 in the Boston–Washington megalopolis] comes to as high as 50% of the solar radiation. Study of climatological effects from re-

leases of this magnitude is far from complete
. . . but there's speculation that the result will
be a unique microclimate for the region un-
related to anything now experienced.
—*Chemical & Engineering News,* March 2, 1970

The message is that the choice between greater energy
consumption and a livable environment must be made
soon. The growth in per capita consumption of energy
documented in Table 9 cannot continue much longer. The
environmental costs of our energy consumption, some of
which are listed above, have generally been externalized;
that is, they haven't been figured into the cost that you
pay for your energy. This situation is not likely to continue. Mine safety regulations, lower sulfur fuels, and
fights over plant location will have the inevitable effect
of pushing up costs—more, probably, than savings in
scale can push them down. In addition, foreign countries will not be willing to let the United States exploit
their energy resources indefinitely.

More and more radical proposals are likely to be heard
in the future. Advertising by public utilities urging increased consumption of energy and thus boosting sales

TABLE 9. GROWTH OF ENERGY CONSUMPTION IN THE U. S.

Year	Total Energy Consumption in (Trillion BTU)	Per Capita Consumption in (Thousand BTU)	Consumption per $ of GNP in (Thousand BTU)
1947	32,870	228,132	106.1
1950	34,153	224,886	96.1
1955	39,956	242,056	91.2
1960	44,816	248,989	91.9
1961	45,573	248,955	91.6
1962	47,620	256,173	89.8
1963	49,649	263,169	90.1
1964	51,515	269,188	88.8
1965	53,791	277,507	87.2
1966	56,948	290,655	86.7
1967	58,873	297,543	87.3
1968	62,432	312,363	88.2
1969*	65,645	325,102	90.2

*Preliminary. GNP in constant 1958 dollars.

Source: These figures were derived from U.S. Government sources
and compiled in *Competition in the Energy Markets,* a report
by the National Economic Research Associates, Inc.

of appliances has already been banned in a few places. Proposals have also been made to invert the rate schedule so that consumption above a specified level costs more per unit of energy, rather than less.

Thus, the environmentally concerned consumer should try to minimize his consumption of power. You can do this in several ways.

■ Transportation accounts for about one quarter of energy consumption in the U.S. (consult Chapter 13). So the less you use your car, the better.

■ You can reduce the amount of energy you use in heating, cooling, lighting, and running the appliances in your home.

■ You can reduce your consumption of products that require a lot of energy in their manufacture. For example, aluminum is made by a process that uses about 10 kilowatt–hours of energy per pound just to recover the free metal from the ore. As Table 9 indicates, the average dollar you spend is accompanied by the spending of about 90,000 BTU of energy somewhere.

TABLE 10. PEAK ELECTRIC CONSUMPTION

	California	Florida	New England
Total sales: (kw–hrs)	38,965,976,000	20,445,172,000	47,386,000,000
Average power: (kilowatts)	4,450,000	2,330,000	5,400,000
Peak power: (kilowatts)	8,666,400	4,563,000	10,045,000
Date of peak:	12–18–68	8–20–68	12–26–68

Sources: The 1968 Annual Reports of Pacific Gas & Electric, Florida Power & Light, and the Electric Council of New England.

■ Peak power demand comes at different times of the year in different parts of the country. Since your electric utility must have enough capacity to meet peak demand with a little to spare, anything you can do to lower that peak demand will help reduce the need to build pump storage facilities and other peaking power installations.

Pollution tends to be worst at peak power times, too. Cutting back on your consumption of energy is a very good way to take action against a whole flock of environmental ills. Such action has the additional advantage of saving you money which you can then spend on more ecologically sound products or pastimes.

WHERE IS "YOUR" ELECTRIC UTILITY AT?*

From the 1969 annual report, Florida Power & Light Company: "Just name it, and it was a year of new high marks in Florida as new people, new business and new industry brought growth in personal income, bank deposits, bank debits, retail sales and so on down the list of the various measurements for prosperity and progress.

"The average annual use of electric service by residential customers reached 9,828 kilowatt hours compared to the national average of 6,550 kilowatt hours. This exceeds all previous power consumption levels and represents a substantial 12 percent jump over 1968.

"Forceful promotion and advertising programs helped our sales allies sell major electric appliances and commercial equipment worth over $275 million—a new all-time high.

"Active promotional efforts also made further inroads into the commercial and industrial markets as more and more businesses switched to electrical applications. A new all-time high in the annual use by commercial customers —an average of 49,166 kilowatt hours—was reached. This also is well above the national average.

"The impact of these sales—particularly of air conditioning units—was underscored by unprecedented use of electric service. Power consumption in July was 28 percent higher than the same month the previous year. New system generation peaks were established 11 times during the summer. The highest occurred on August 20, when the system registered a 4,563,000 kilowatt demand.

"In a world increasingly concerned about the quality

* Note: This account is not meant to characterize all utilities.

of the environment, FPL is sharply aware of its responsibility to help protect and enhance the natural surroundings even as it works to expand necessary facilities to serve its customers.

"To help safeguard water standards, FPL is financing a variety of studies at the Turkey Point plant in South Florida to determine if power plant operation has any significant "thermal effects" on marine life. The studies will serve as a guide in operating the plant in harmony with the natural surroundings."

From The New York Times, *March 14, 1970:*
"The Department of Justice filed suit today to halt present and future thermal pollution of Biscayne Bay by the Florida Power and Light Company, the state's largest power company.

"The suit was filed at the request of Secretary of the Interior Walter J. Hickel who said the operation of the company's two fossil fuel plants at Turkey Point and the two nuclear power plants now under construction there would contravene 'the interest of the United States in the fragile ecology of Biscayne National Monument,' established by Congress in 1968.

"Mr. Hickel requested the filing of a suit after he and Gov. Claude R. Kirk Jr. had failed last month to get satisfactory assurances from the company that it would take measures to keep the thermal pollution of the bay within limits prescribed by the Federal Government.

"In 1968, a year after the two plants went into full operation, the complaint stated, the thermal pollution had created a 'barren area' of 300 acres. This had more than doubled by 1969, according to the complaint.

"The situation would become much worse, the complaint stated, when the two nuclear reactors are in operation. To cool these units, the total water withdrawn from the bay would amount to 4.5 million gallons a minute.

" 'At this rate,' the Justice Department said, 'water equivalent to all of Biscayne Bay would pass through the plant and its works in less than a month. The high water velocities will scour and disturb an extensive area of bay bottom. The removal of microlife will destroy the existing ecological cycle. The plankton and other small sea life that was cooked to death in passing through the plant would be discharged into Card Sound as organic refuse.'

"Biscayne Bay has 58 species of fish, more than 100 of shell fish and a dozen species of birds, including pelicans, cormorants, herons, egrets and the rare roseate spoonbill."

COMPARING ENERGY CONSUMPTION

You can compare the relative energy consumption of appliances that use different energy sources by using the conversions listed in Table 11.

TABLE 11. ENERGY EQUIVALENTS

1 Therm	=	100,000 BTU
1 KWH (100% conversion)	=	3,413 BTU
1 lb. Propane Gas	=	21,650 BTU
1 cu ft Propane Gas	=	2,500 BTU
1 lb Butane Gas	=	21,500 BTU
1 cu ft Butane Gas	=	3,200 BTU
1 cu ft Natural Gas	=	1,050 BTU
1 gallon #1 Domestic Fuel Oil	=	132,900–138,800 BTU
1 gallon #2 Domestic Fuel Oil	=	135,800–144,300 BTU
1 gallon gasoline	=	126,000 BTU
1 lb bituminous coal	=	13,100 BTU

To convert electric energy use in KWH to the BTU equivalent of the fuel used to generate it, you should correct for the efficiency of the conversion. Utilities usually report the relevant figure in their annual reports as "BTU per net KWH generated." It is in the neighborhood of 1 KWH = 10,371 BTU (1968 national average). Thus, a gas water heater that uses 270 Therms of fuel energy in a year (27.0 million BTU) uses less energy than an electric water heater that consumes 4,219 KWH (4,219 × 10,371 = 43.8 million BTU).

WATCH THE ENERGY FLOW INTO YOUR HOME

To get something approaching a tangible feeling for the electricity you use, locate the electric meter in your home. The faster its small disc turns, the more energy your home is using. Try to turn everything off, then watch what happens when the refrigerator kicks on or off. Try turning on a light, the television, or the toaster. The meter register gives a reading of how many kilowatt hours of energy flows into your home.

In a similar way you can watch the cubic feet of natural gas flow into your home to run the stove, hot-water heater, or furnace.

ELECTRIC APPLIANCES

There was once a time when clocks were wound by hand, when water pumps had handles, when clothes were hung outside to be dried, disinfected, and freshened by the sun, and when windmill and waterwheel put the elements to work for us. Today *everything* has to have a plug attached to it. To get an idea of how far this has gone, take an inventory of your own home. Go to the electrical outlets, follow the wires, and see where they lead. Try it.

Attached to the business end of many you will probably find lamps. In the kitchen you are likely to find an electric stove, oven, refrigerator, freezer, dishwasher, disposal unit, toaster, rotisserie, broiler, griddle, food warmer, bottle warmer, blender, mixer, percolator, can opener or carving knife. The bathroom has outlets for an electric shaver, toothbrush, water pick, curlers, hair setter, drier, and even an electric comb. The laundry room may contain a washer, dryer, and hot-water heater. The house may have electric heat for cold weather and an air conditioner for hot, a humidifier for upstairs and a de-humidifier for the basement. Elsewhere there are electric

clocks, irons, a sunlamp, fan, vacuum cleaner, rug sham-
pooer, typewriter, blanket, sewing machine, room heater,
and power tools. Entertainment would not be possible
without the radio, television, hi–fi set, and an electric
organ, guitar, or banjo. Today, the prospective environmentalist is being told he needs a private electric or gas
incinerator and—for the most up–to–date—a compactor
unit for the garbage. Tomorrow it's the car. And what's
been left out? The electric lawn mower, trimmer, and
hedge clipper. There is even an electric–powered jack
that plugs into the cigarette lighter in the car.

Hold it! Imagine what happens if the dehumidifier
has to dehumidify the humidifier's humidity because someone forgets to close the door between the two machines.

What happens if you follow the wires to the other end?
Surprise! It's PG&E or Consolidated Edison. Overhead
wires pass through rows of disfigured shade and ornamental trees to enormous, landscape–disfiguring overhead
distribution towers. Hydroelectric dams are on the other
end, behind them inundated valleys. So are fossil fuel
plants with smoking stacks spewing out SO_2, or nuclear
power plants heating up a river, wild places having been
invaded so that their pump storage facilities could be
built. The wires go to Niagara Falls, to Glen Canyon, to
Grand Coulee or the T.V.A. Ask a Californian about
Bodega Bay, a New Yorker about Storm King, an Alas-
kan about Ramparts Dam, or an Arizonan about Marble
Gorge and Bridge Canyon.

Certainly the electric utility has proven to be a mixed
blessing. Today's lamps give light without the soot produced by an oil lamp, yet some scientists are beginning to
look into the possibility of ("light pollution.") No one can
deny the convenience of many appliances, but kitchen
blenders screech at 93 decibels (above the "discomfort"
level of 80 decibels), and electronic rock music hits our
ears at 115 decibels. Television has assumed a major communications and entertainment role. The effect that this
machine alone has had on our modern life style—on
participatory sports, the arts, and reading—is staggering.

So what can the consumer do? Will he need to rewire

his home every ten years to fill a "housepower gap?" What are the alternatives? It is a fact that not so long ago—even last year—you got along with less per capita power consumption and thus less air pollution from power generation.

Do you need these?   Explore the following list and decide which of the items on it are essential and which are merely "convenient."

- Electric comb
- Electric knife or carver
- Electric charcoal starter
- Electric can opener
- Electric broiler (besides the broiler in your oven)
- Electric hedge trimmers
- Power lawnmower
- Electric shaver
- Higher intensity lighting
- Home garbage compactor
- Home incinerator
- Total air conditioning
- Food waste disposal unit

There are non-polluting alternatives to each of these that consume less energy and cost less to buy and to operate.

If you have it, do you need to use it?   Many of the machines in the home are used far more than they need to be—simply because there is little incentive not to do so. How about trying the following:

- Don't turn on the dishwasher or the washing machine until you have a full load.
- If you live in an area where the air is clean, why use your clothes dryer on a sunny day? Hang the clothes outside, and see how fresh they smell when you take them in.
- Turn off unneeded lights.
- Don't use your waste disposal unit when you can create a compost pile with the garbage instead.

Can you share it?   Not everyone needs to have exclusive ownership of everything. We have seen what

happens when everyone has a car. What can you arrange
to share?
- A lawn mower?
- A magazine or newspaper subscription?
- A washing machine or dryer?

*If you are buying an appliance, do you need the extra
feature?*
- The pre–soak cycle in a washing machine?
- The automatic ice cube maker for the refrigerator?
- The self–cleaning oven?
- The second hundred watts in the hi–fi system?
- The rinse agent dispenser for your dishwasher?
- The refrigerator quick–chill compartment?

TABLE 12. ESTIMATED POWER CONSUMPTION OF ELECTRIC APPLIANCES

Appliance	Average Wattage	Estimated Use	Estimated KWH Consumed Annually
Broiler	1,436	80 min/week	100
Carving Knife	92	104 min/week	8
Coffee Maker	894	20 min/day	106
Deep Fat Fryer	1,448	66 min/week	83
Dishwasher	1,201	50 min/day	363
Food Blender	386	6 min/day	15
Food Mixer	127	17 min/day	13
Food Waste Disposer	445	11 min/day	30
Frying Pan	1,196	26 min/day	186
Hot Plate	1,257	12 min/day	90
Range	12,207	16 min/day	1,175
Roaster	1,333	25 min/day	205
Toaster	1,146	5.6 min/day	39
Waffle Iron	1,116	23 min/week	22
Food Freezer (15 cu ft)	341	40% of the time	1,195
Food Freezer (Frostless 15 cu ft)	440	46% of the time	1,761
Refrigerator (12 cu ft)	241	34% of the time	728
Refrigerator (Frostless 12 cu ft)	321	43% of the time	1,217
Refrigerator–Freezer (14 cu ft)	326	40% of the time	1,137
Refrigerator–Freezer (Frostless 14 cu ft)	615	34% of the time	1,829
Clothes Dryer	4,856	34 min/day	993
Iron (hand)	1,008	23 min/day	144
Washing Machine (automatic)	512	33 min/day	103

Appliance	Average Wattage	Estimated Use	Estimated KWH Consumed Annually
Washing Machine (non-automatic)	286	44 min/day	76
Air Conditioner (room)	1,566	10% of the time	1,389
Bed Covering	177	2.3 hours/day	147
Dehumidifier	257	40% of the time	377
Fan (attic)	370	2.2 hours/day	291
Fan (roll-about)	171	2.2 hours/day	138
Hair Dryer	381	42 min/week	14
Heat Pump	11,848	3.7 hours/day	16,003
Heater (radiant)	1,322	22 min/day	176
Humidifier	117	16% of the time	163
Shaver	14	210 min/day	18
Sun Lamp	279	66 min/week	16
Tooth Brush	7	117 min/day	5
Water Heater (standard)	2,475	4.7 hours/day	4,219
Water Heater (quick recovery)	4,474	2.9 hours/day	4,811
Radio	71	3.3 hours/day	86
Television (black & white)	237	4.2 hours/day	362
Television (color)	332	4.1 hours/day	502
Clock	2	100% of the time	17
Sewing Machine	75	2.8 hours/week	11
Vacuum Cleaner	630	84 min/week	46

Source: Edison Electric Institute, national averages

Lighting

No one lights his home with anything but electricity any longer—a good development, everything considered. Gas and oil lamps and candles created a good deal of pollution and were a safety hazard. They did have one advantage, however, and that was that the supply of candles, oil, and tallow was always finite. There were very tangible reasons to conserve.

Today we can be prodigal and never know the difference. How many unnecessary lights does your family leave on? Each ceiling light uses 75 to several hundred watts of power, each lamp 60 to 200 watts. One unneeded 100 watt bulb left on all day uses 2.4 KWH. That is 876 KWH a year or enough to run almost any one of the appliances in Table 12 for a year. At 3¢ per KWH that adds $26 to your yearly electric bill: and the environment, *your* environment must absorb the costs that go with those extra 876 KWH.

Here are some of the ways you can reduce your consumption of energy in the home.

▪ Turn off lights when they are not needed.

▪ During the day, open the drapes and blinds and use the natural light that is free and non–polluting.

▪ Different tasks require different amounts of light. Table 13 indicates representative minimum levels of illumination recommended by the Illuminating Engineering Society. Note that general lighting levels can (and should) be less intense.

▪ The color and finish of the walls, ceiling, floors, and furniture control light intensity and texture. Keep this in mind in decorating your home and in choosing a work-place.

▪ Replace high-wattage bulbs with lower wattage bulbs where the high-intensity light is not needed.

TABLE 13. MINIMUM RECOMMENDED LEVELS OF ILLUMINATION

TASK	LIGHT INTENSITY (In foot–candles)
Reading and writing:	
Handwriting, indistinct print	70
Books, magazines, newspapers	30
Recreation:	
Playing cards, tables, billiards	30
Table tennis	20
Grooming:	50
Kitchen work:	
At sink	70
At work counters	50
Laundering jobs:	
At washer	50
At ironing board	50
Sewing:	
Dark fabrics (fine detail, low contrast)	200
Prolonged periods (light-to-medium fabrics)	100
Occasional (light-colored fabrics)	50
Handicraft:	
Close work (reading diagrams, fine finishing)	100
Measuring, sawing, assembling	50
General lighting:	
Any area involving a visual task	30
For safety in passage areas	10
Areas used mostly for relaxation, recreation, and conversation	10

Source: "Planning Your Home Lighting," *Home and Garden Bulletin No. 138*, U.S. Department of Agriculture.

■ Fluorescent lighting is significantly more efficient than normal incandescent lighting—about 62 lumens per watt vs. 14 lumens per watt. Fluorescent bulbs also produce less waste heat and last seven to ten times as long as incandescent bulbs.

■ Keep your lighting fixtures clean so that you get all the light you should.

Refrigerators

Refrigerators and freezers are indispensable to the modern homekeeper. They permit him to buy in quantity and to reduce food spoilage. To the extent that they cut down on trips to the supermarket, they reduce automobile pollution. In 1968, 81.3% of American households *owned* a refrigerator or freezer, and 99.8% of wired homes were equipped with one.

What might the environmental drawbacks be? The author recalls the visit of a junk man about fifteen years ago. He came to cart away an old refrigerator and in the process he destroyed a good axe chopping the thing apart and killed some forsythia bushes when the toxic compressor gas escaped. Although the machines have a relatively long life, when they do expire they have to go somewhere. Too often they end up as unreclaimed waste metal, posing a hazard of suffocation for playing children who get locked inside.

Most refrigerators and freezers are run by electric power. The consumer magazines variously estimate operating costs to be from $3 to $7.50 per month at 3¢ per kilowatt-hour. That means 3.3 to 8.3 KWH per day to operate the beast. Power costs for the side–by–side models which are reportedly gaining in popularity are about 45% higher than for standard models. They are also noisier. Thus you can make an environmental contribution by foregoing the dubious convenience and extra expense of the side–by–side model. You can also reduce power consumption by avoiding some of the optional gadgets, such as automatic ice–makers (which also use up space) and quick–freezing compartments. Most units have heaters that help reduce the problem of sweating when humidity is high. Sometimes there is an "economy switch" that lets you save money when humidity is low. It also saves power if you situate your refrigerator away from direct sunlight and radiators.

A last, rather subtle point concerns frost–free refrigerators. Food tends to dry out in these unless it is covered. This has the disadvantage of increasing your use of plastic wrappings. You can counter this by employing reusable containers. As Table 12 indicates, the frostless models use considerably more energy.

Ranges and ovens

The modern range with oven is much more efficient than its primitive equivalent, the campfire, or than the charcoal grill. The major choice the buyer must make is between gas and electric ranges.

The inherently lower efficiency of electric power is largely compensated for by the greater efficiency of the electric heating element and the electric oven. The *Consumer Bulletin Annual* estimates 75% efficiency for the electric element versus 40% for the gas burner. Similarly, the electric oven, which is relatively airtight, throws off much less waste heat than the gas oven, which must cycle fresh air through the oven to keep a proper mixture for combustion at the burner. Thus, the electric range and oven would be favored in hot climates and the gas in cooler climates. Based on industry data, total energy consumption for the two appliances is similar (Gas range at 105 Therms per year $= 10.5$ million BTU versus electric range at 1,175 KWH per year $= 1,175 \times 10,371 = 12.2$ million BTU).

The self-cleaning oven. Both gas and electric ovens are available now with a self–cleaning feature. The oven temperature is raised to about 900°F. for 2 to 3 hours during the cleaning cycle, and any dirt is reduced to a fine ash. The energy consumption during such a cycle is 3 to 4.5 KWH of electric energy or about 0.4 Therms of gas, roughly similar. The alternative to the self–cleaning oven involves the use of caustic, hazardous chemical cleaners that may come in undesirable aerosol containers. The chemical method is also infinitely grubbier.

Precisely because the self–cleaning oven is so convenient, it is necessary to warn against overuse. Another factor is that, whereas ovens used to be dark and unlit, today they are bright and well–lit, an inducement to overuse the cleaning feature. Keep in mind that ovens operate at temperatures that are high enough to kill most germs. Keep your oven clean, but clean it periodically, not frequently.

Dishwashers

Washing dishes has to be one of the most unloved tasks in the home. What are the options you have in dealing with the problem?

Using disposable cups, plates, utensils, and prepared foods is not an environmentally sound alternative. It is expensive and badly compounds the solid waste problem. Similarly, lining pans and broilers with aluminum foil is a harmful, though common, practice. While it may mitigate the hassle of washing that pan, it also adds a piece of non–biodegradable aluminum foil to the trash pile.

Washing dishes by hand permits you to minimize use of water. If you employ this method and especially if you live in an area where clean water is not plentiful, try consciously to conserve water. Don't run the rinse water continuously.

Hand washing also means that the detergents you use are less polluting. *Joy, Dove, Amway Dish Drops, Trend, Ivory Liquid, SweetHeart Dishwashing Liquid,* and most other products specifically designed for hand washing have no phosphates.

In contrast to the products designed for hand washing of dishes, present automatic dishwasher detergents have some of the highest phosphate levels. (See p. 168) This is because dishwashers must be low–sudsing and must take all of the hardness out of the water to avoid leaving spots when the dishes are dried.

There are several things you can do to diminish environmental damage from dishwashers if you own one:

■ Use a minimal amount of detergent.

■ Use a detergent that is formulated for the degree of water hardness in your area. For example, Electrasol has two formulations (soft—5.54%P, and hard—8.92%P) and Finish has three (soft—4.53%P, medium—7.26%P, and hard—10.89%P). Ask your grocer which formulation is sold in your area.

■ Your washer probably has a drying cycle. You can conserve power and still have dry dishes by interrupting it partway through this cycle, or you can cut the cycle out entirely and hand–dry the load. The latter is a better way of getting around the problem of spotty glassware than is the use of a high–phosphate rinse agent.

■ Use the dishwasher only when you have a full load, since each cycle uses *twelve to sixteen gallons of water.* Buy the machine that uses the smallest amount of water.

■ High temperature sani-cycles are optional on some makes. These boost power consumption and are not really necessary.

Food waste disposers

Food waste disposers are ecologically undesirable. Their job is to reduce food wastes to a slurry which can be flushed into a sewer system and from there—most likely—into a nearby body of water. Garbage handled in this way contributes to the aging of your streams and lakes. Instead, the organic matter and minerals should be returned to the soil to replenish and fertilize it.

Food waste disposer units cannot be used if you have a cesspool, and they add 20% to 25% to the load of your septic tank or your municipal sewage treatment facility. In the latter case, the extra cost is taken out in taxes. New York City bans them. Also, as anyone who has used one can attest, food waste disposers add many decibels to the noise–pollution level of the home.

Investigate the alternatives. Even if you have a waste disposer, you don't have to use it.

■ If you live in a rural or suburban area, you should be able to compost your garbage (see page 79).

■ If you live in a city, find out how your garbage and your waste water are handled. If your garbage goes to a rat-infested dump and your waste water to a secondary and tertiary treatment facility, it might make sense to use a waste disposer.

Clothes washers

The job of the washing machine is basically very simple: to agitate the clothes in a wash liquor that frees the dirt; to rinse away the dirty water; and to free the clothes of excess water before their final drying. The range of options is wide—from the scrub board through the wringer-washer (about 400,000 of which are still sold each year) to the elaborately "programmed" machines that automatically vary water temperatures and offer pre-soak cycles and extra rinses. Advanced models automatically dispense detergent, bleach, and fabric softeners at the proper moment and permit you to vary the water level.

Environmentally speaking, power consumption is probably less of a problem with washers than is water use and pollution. Most machines seem to use about 45 gallons of water for a 12-pound load, and, of course, more with extra rinses. Some can be purchased with a "suds saver" feature that lets you reuse wash water. Most new models let you vary the water level to match the load—a useful feature. In general, however, American models are profligate water users when compared with foreign models.

When you shop for a washing machine, look for one that will enable you to limit your use of water. The annual buyer's guides put out by *Consumer Reports* and *Consumer Bulletin* provide tables that indicate water use for each type.

The condition of the waste water depends on what you add to it.

Eutrophication of lakes and rivers due to phosphates in laundry products is a very serious problem. You can reduce your contribution to water pollution by using soap instead of detergent and by skipping extra steps that are actually unnecessary, such as the high-phosphate enzyme presoak and the addition of fabric softener. Hard water presents a problem that can be met either by using a home water softener or by adding a non-polluting softener—like washing soda—to each load.

Clothes dryers

Drying clothes in a machine uses a good bit of energy —about 2 to 4 kw hr per 7-pound load. That energy can be delivered either as electricity or as natural gas. Of course the electricity is generated somewhere, either by burning natural gas or by some other means that is probably more polluting. The energy in the gas is more efficiently used by a gas dryer. In most areas the gas dryer is also less expensive to operate.

The fancy new dryers offer several options. "Soft heat" gradually lowers the heat as the clothes dry. This is to protect the new no-iron fabrics. Some machines also tumble the load briefly every five minutes after the load is dry until the clothes are removed, again to keep permanent-press articles from wrinkling. This saves on ironing.

There is, however, a much better alternative to the clothes dryer, and that is the clothesline. Non-polluting except perhaps for a little visual pollution, this method disinfects and freshens the fabrics very effectively and at rock-bottom cost. Even if you have a dryer, hang your clothes out to dry whenever the weather is right.

Room air conditioners

Cooling of the home was discussed in a previous chapter (page 39), where it was mentioned that air conditioners use a good bit of power. *Consumer Reports* estimates operating costs of the standard 6000 BTU room air conditioner for 10 hours a day with the compressor on 70% of the time at $5.60 to $5.98 a month. (3¢ per KWH.) That is 187 to 199 KWH of electric energy per month.

If you decide that you need an air conditioner to survive, get one that will cool only one room and center your activities there when the weather is hot. In choosing the model, consult the table that *Consumer Reports* has published. It permits you to calculate the cooling capacity you need, taking into account the size of the room, the window exposure, the insulation of the room, and the heat generated by people and electrical equipment. Their formulas indicate, for instance, that a lone person doing the ironing (1000 watts) under a 100-watt light bulb and watching a color television set (350 watts) would have to allow nearly 5000 BTU per hour capacity just to counteract the heat generated by presence of the person and the three pieces of electrical equipment.

6. WATER USE IN THE HOME

6. Water Use in the Home

WATER USE—AN OVERVIEW

It is obvious that you use water when you flush the toilet, take a shower, or turn on a faucet. It is less obvious that you also consume water when you buy a newspaper, but you do. Somewhere, a paper plant is fouling a stream to make the newsprint that you will use tomorrow. It takes water to manufacture most of the things that you buy; lots of it. Anyone who lives near an industrial plant—a paper mill, steel plant, or chemical plant—knows only too well what a pound of newsprint, steel, or plastic means in terms of polluted air and water. Table 14 gives a broad indication of where water pollution comes from.

One would think that with an average of 30 inches of rain per year in the continental United States—5 trillion gallons per day or 1.2 trillion gallons after evaporation and transpiration losses—there would be enough water to satisfy all of our needs. But 1.2 trillion gallons divided by 200 million people is only 6000 gallons per person per day. Consider what claims are put on that 6000 gallons.

You drink half a gallon of water each day.

The food you eat costs water to produce. Plants take in water through their roots and release it to the atmosphere in the process called transpiration. The water cost for a day's supply of vegetables and grain is in the neighborhood of 200 or 300 gallons. A standard daily American ration of 9.4 ounces of meat adds about 1400 gallons. Thus, use of surface water runoff for irrigation can draw upon a significant portion of the 6000 gallons.

You draw on the order of 100 gallons of water each day for residential use. This water must be pure.

The water that you return to the system through the sewer is, of course, not pure. Typical municipal sewage loads are 120 gallons of waste water per capita per day, containing 1/5 pound of suspended solids and 1/6 pound of biological oxygen demand (BOD). BOD is a measure of the amount of oxygen that is needed by the microorganisms that break down the biodegradable wastes.

Industrial waste creates a load that before treatment is double or triple the municipal sewage load. In addition, industry throws chemical pollutants into the water supply that are not biodegradable, such as mercury for example.

The growth of livestock feedlots has added another dimension. It used to be that animal manure was recycled back to the land. Now, however, transporting it back to the farm is out of the question. Oxygen demand from manure disposal also exceeds the municipal load.

A complicating factor is the growing use of water for cooling purposes. Thermal power plants now use about one tenth of the average U.S. runoff for this purpose. Although this doesn't add pollutants as such, heating the water does remove oxygen, thereby reducing the capacity of the water to assimilate other wastes. (Note: Chlorine added to the intake water to prevent fouling does kill pollution-digesting bacteria.)

Additional contamination from pesticide residues, acid mine drainage, oil spillage, agricultural fertilizer runoff, and the natural leaching of salts from soil adds to the burden your 6000 gallons must bear.

And don't forget that other creatures must use this same water. The finfish, waterfowl, and shellfish that inhabit the inland rivers and lakes and the estuarine regions have a claim on clean water, too, as do the land animals that drink it.

Unlike energy, water is not consumed; it is used. With proper management, the 6000 gallons of water can be stretched into considerably more. It depends on *how* it is used.

Treating our rivers and lakes as sewers into which all wastes can be poured counts on dilution; but a body of water has a limited capacity to absorb pollution. As Garrett Hardin described it in "The Tragedy of the Commons," (*Science* magazine, Dec. 13, 1968), many of our rivers and lakes have been so violated that they have lost the ability to cleanse themselves. Barry Commoner has calculated that by 1980 the oxygen demands from municipal wastes alone will equal the oxygen content of the total flow of all U.S. rivers during the summer months.

A distinction should be made between surface water and groundwater. Since gross pollution has already destroyed much of our surface water supply, to meet residential water needs, many communities have turned to drilling wells to tap the groundwater supply. Fortunately, soil is an excellent filter that screens out essentially all pollutants. However, it takes a fair amount of land to provide enough groundwater for very many people. In Massachussetts, a state with higher-than-average rainfall and good glacial soils, a family uses the amount of water collected by about one acre of land. The dwindling supply of unpolluted surface water and the limited supply of groundwater conspire to make the supply of municipal water very short in most metropolitan areas.

In some sections of the country, water must be brought hundreds of miles to meet the needs of expanding urban populations. Quite a few of the battles waged by traditional conservationists have been about water plans. We lost a second Yosemite Valley in the Sierra when Hetch Hetchy Valley was dammed to form a reservoir for San Francisco. We almost lost the Grand Canyon to the Arizona Water Plan. And today conservationists are actively trying to preserve the integrity of the water systems in the Everglades, Northern Florida, the San Francisco Bay region, and elsewhere.

You can see that decisions regarding home water use are, like most ecological problems, intimately interconnected with many other decisions you must make. If you want to make a personal contribution to the battle to preserve a clean water supply, consider the following possibilities.

WATER CONSERVATION IN THE HOME

Minimize the amount of water you use and the waste burden you impose on the sewer system.

- Fix leaky faucets and toilets. The steady flow uses up a considerable volume.
- Any appliance that uses water should be operated only at full capacity. A dishwasher uses about 14 gallons of water whether it washes a full load or one glass. A clothes washer uses about 45 gallons of water for a 12-pound load. Consult pages 99 and 100 for more suggestions.
- Food waste disposal units are about as ecologically unsound as an appliance can get. A disposal unit will increase the load you impose on the sewage system by 25%. (See page 100.)
- Don't run the water unnecessarily. For example, don't keep the water running the whole time you are brushing your teeth.
- Follow the now-classic suggestion of placing a brick or two in your toilet to reduce the amount of water that machine uses.
- Try the shower vs. bath test. Take a shower and see how high the water level comes with the plug in the drain. If you use less water taking a bath, then take baths. If you can't stand the thought of losing your shower, then reduce the amount of water you use showering. Adjust the shower head to a finer spray or replace the shower head if you must. Try the ultimate, the Navy shower—wet yourself, turn off the water, lather, and rinse. (It is interesting to note the Japanese method of public bathing. The bather draws a small bucket of water from a faucet and uses this to wet himself, lather, and rinse. Once clean, he adjourns to a steaming hot tub of water where he can luxuriate. This tub serves many; only enough water to keep it hot need be added.)
- The amount of soap, bubble bath, and water conditioners you use during a shower, a bath, or doing a load

of clothes or dishes is probably as important as how much water you use. Consult page 157 and ff. for more information on soaps and detergents.

▪ If you live in a hard-water area, you may want to install a water conditioner. By removing calcium and magnesium ions a water conditioner reduces the amount of soap and detergent you must use. The removal is effected by exchanging the "hard" ions with sodium ions; during recharge of the exchanger salts are actually added to the water supply. Keep this in mind when you consider automatic vs. manual models. Conditioned water is not demineralized water or distilled. It shouldn't be used for watering plants and lawns or by anyone on a low-sodium diet.

▪ A recent Environment Control Administration survey indicated that 30% of 3563 samples taken from public water supplies in nine metropolitan areas and Vermont contained germs and chemicals in excess of one federal standard or another. In the light of this sort of evidence you might wish to consider a home water purifier; however, such devices are expensive. Generally they rely on technologies that are best understood by experts. It is very difficult for the lay person to judge advertising claims. If you suspect your water supply is polluted in any way, have it analyzed (see the *Yellow Pages* under *Laboratories-Testing* or *Chemists-Analytical & Consulting*). Communicate the results to the municipal public works commissioner. If necessary, buy drinking water bottled in large returnable jugs.

▪ Like electric power, water use has periods of peak demands. Municipal water system design criteria generally provide for at least double the average demand for maximum daily loads and five times the average for hourly peaks. In residential areas where lawn watering is common in the summer, even these limits are sometimes exceeded. Water-cooled air conditioning can also require a lot of water. During the summer months hourly water use is generally high between 7 a.m. and 10 p.m., peaking in the early evening and, on Saturday and Sunday, at mid-day. Water your lawn—if you must—during non-peak periods.

■ Plant lawn covers and shrubs that will be able to get along with a minimal amount of sprinkling.

■ Don't move where water is scarce.

■ Don't use your sink as a dump. Refrain from washing garbage, detergents, and chemicals (*e.g.,* Drāno) into the sewers as much as you can.

■ Never use pesticides in such a way that they could contaminate either ground or surface water.

■ Don't use salts in the winter to free walkways of ice. This practice is ruining a growing number of wells in New England.

CONSERVING MUNICIPAL WATER

Encourage your town to act to protect its water supply.

■ Introduce water metering. Areas with metered water have been found to use considerably less water than flat-rate areas. If you don't pay for the water on a monthly billing, you pay for it through taxes.

■ Encourage your municipality to employ tertiary treatment of its sewage. Primary treatment only settles out the solids. Secondary treatment gives the bacteria a chance to remove some of the oxygen demand but leaves the water nutrient-rich and thus contributes to eutrophication. Tertiary treatment removes these nutrients which never should have been dumped into the water supply in the first place.

■ One of the best methods of waste water treatment is land disposal, either by sprinkling or by irrigation. The wastes are broken down in the soil, where they act as fertilizer, and the water soaks in to recharge the ground water supply.

PROTECT GROUNDWATER

The protection of groundwater from pollution has many aspects.

■ Your community should identify the prime recharge areas and zone them protectively.

■ Don't fill marshes and don't build on floodplains. Avoid paving.

■ If you live in a suburb and have enough land and proper soil conditions, you should be able to use a septic tank. The septic tank consists of an underground basin where the sewage from your home is collected. There it is decomposed by bacteria. It also has a percolation system that returns the water to the groundwater system. Impurities are filtered out by the soil immediately around the tank. (Nevertheless, it is wise to locate the septic tank away from any wells.)

REDUCE YOUR SHARE OF INDUSTRY'S WATER USE

Table 14 indicates that the biggest polluters are food-processing, paper, chemical, and metal plants. Reducing unnecessary consumption in these areas will thus reduce your use of water.

■ Don't use colored disposable paper products. The dyes pollute.

■ Reduce your consumption of electricity. In this way you can help lessen the thermal pollution load on waters.

■ Industry can drastically reduce the pollution burden it puts on surface waters. In-plant recycling of water and waste treatment will come if you apply heavy pressure through government and by publicizing the "bad guys."

■ Discourage deep-well disposal of noxious chemicals and radioactive wastes. Given enough time they will find their way into any nearby groundwater. Deep-disposal wells are considered highly unstable by responsible geologists. They have erupted into geysers and caused earthquakes and releases of explosives gases.

To summarize, reduce your use of water and don't pollute. With proper management, there should be enough water to meet all of our needs—swimming, boating, and fishing included.

TABLE 14. ESTIMATED VOLUME OF INDUSTRIAL WASTES
BEFORE TREATMENT, 1964

INDUSTRY	WASTE WATER VOLUME (BILLIONS OF GALLONS)	BOD₅* (MILLIONS OF POUNDS)	SUSPENDED SOLIDS (MILLIONS OF POUNDS)
Food & Kindred Products	690	4,300	6,600
Meat Products	99	640	640
Dairy Products	58	400	230
Canned & Frozen Food	87	1,200	600
Sugar Refining	220	1,400	5,000
All Other	220	670	110
Textile Mill Products	140	890	N.E.
Paper & Allied Products	1,900	5,900	3,000
Chemical & Allied Products	3,700	9,700	1,900
Petroleum & Coal	1,300	500	460
Rubber & Plastics	160	40	50
Primary Metals	4,300	480	4,700
Blast Furnaces & Steel Mills	3,600	160	4,300
All Other	740	320	430
Machinery	150	60	50
Electrical Machinery	91	70	20
Transportation Equipment	240	120	N.E.
All Other Manufacturing	450	390	930
All Manufacturing	13,100	22,000	18,000
For Comparison: Sewered Population of U.S.	5,300	7,300	8,800

Source: *The Cost of Clean Water*, Volume II, page 63, Federal Water
Pollution Control Administration, U.S. Department of the
Interior (1968)

*BOD = Biological oxygen demand. BOD is a measure of the amount
of oxygen needed by the microorganisms that break down biodegradable
wastes.

7.   MANAGING WASTE IN THE HOME

7. Managing Waste in the Home

We all take municipal refuse collection and disposal, like most public services, too much for granted. We shouldn't. It costs us collectively in excess of $3 billion per year, more than anything else except schools and roads. While vastly greater quantities of solid wastes are generated by our mines and farms, it is the several hundred million tons produced each year in our homes and businesses and collected by municipal garbage collectors that contributes most heavily to the many environmental crises we face today.

We don't become aware of this until there is a major breakdown in the system, such as a strike, or the day the public works commissioner tells his city that there is no more room in the dump. This is happening more and more frequently. People are gradually becoming aware that the pollution problems associated with waste disposal—smoke from open burning, seepage of polluted water from dumps, rodent infestations, and the disappearance of ecologically valuable wetlands under landfill—are acute problems that must be dealt with now if we hope to preserve the qualities of a livable environment.

While the power to decide many of the major environmental questions resides in remote corporate board rooms or at the state and national levels of government, solid waste is handled almost exclusively at the local level. This is both a help and a hindrance. It's a help in that it gives a concerned individual potentially easier access to the public official who makes the decisions. It is a hindrance because enough concerned citizens are needed to promote rational community plans for solid waste disposal in *every* community.

117

You, too, have a part to play. Promote recycling and salvage in any way you can. If your community uses an open dump, as most do, try to promote the far-less-polluting technique of sanitary landfill. If your community incinerates, it can use the resulting heat to generate electricity and can also reclaim the residue; new technologies have found uses for such materials. Compaction is a way to reduce the volume of the waste load, but, as with landfill, the material is taken out of the ecological cycle. Composting, on the other hand, brings decomposable materials back into the cycle. So does incineration.

There are significant technological developments in the works. Among them is central waste disposal, a contract service that will apply new waste disposal technologies to refuse collected from a whole region.

In this chapter, we look at some of the ways in which you can reduce your own contribution to the solid waste problem. If you are an average American, about five pounds of the trash and garbage that is collected each day is yours. You can reduce this substantially, and you can adopt practices in your own home that will facilitate recycling and re-use.

TABLE 15. GENERATION OF SOLID WASTES, 1967

SOURCE	PER CAPITA POUNDS PER DAY	TOTAL MILLIONS OF TONS PER YEAR
Municipal*	5.8	212
Domestic	3.5	......
Commercial	2.3	......
Miscellaneous urban	1.2	44
Industrial	3.0	110
Federal	1.2	43
Mineral	30.8	1126
Agricultural	58.0	2115
Vegetable	15.0	......
Animal	43.0	......

*Note: Actual collection was only 4.23 pounds per person per day.

Source: "Solid Waste Management," Office of Science and Technology, May 1969.

REDUCE CONSUMPTION

Take an inventory of what comes into your house and what leaves it. How many things pass through it essentially unchanged and unused? How many magazines are unread? How many clothes and toys and appliances are thrown out that someone else could use or that could be fixed?

We throw away more and more; supposedly this is a sign of our increasing affluence. In 1920, the figure was 2.75 pounds per person per day; today it is about 5 pounds and in 1980 it is projected to be about 8 pounds of trash for each of us. The International Paper Company joyfully announces "The Disposable Environment:"

> "Tomorrow's baby may live in the same house you do. But he'll probably live in a totally different world from the one you live in. Because everything the baby wears or touches —virtually the entire environment in which he lives—can be disposable."

> "Disposable obstetrical delivery packs, diapers, wardrobe, sheets, blankets, and even nursery furniture.

> "And by the time today's baby grows up, there's a good chance he may be moving into an entire paper world. Curtains, carpets, furniture, even whole houses made of 'paper' will be taken for granted in the future.

> "The disposable environment—the kind of fresh thinking we bring to every problem."

One wonders whether International Paper's vision of the future provides us with paper "trees" to replace the forests that are used up by their products and paper fences to screen the massive dumps from our eyes.

The disposable world is closer than you might think.

Visit a hospital. There, heavy use of disposables generates 15 to 18 pounds of garbage per day per average patient. Plastics, polyvinyl chloride, and metal syringes create special complications above and beyond the problem of sheer volume.

But we don't have to live in this wasteful way. You can reduce your production of trash in many ways.

Cut down on your use of disposables:

■ Use cloth napkins, handtowels, handkerchiefs, and diapers instead of throw-away paper ones.

■ Don't use paper towels to sop up a spill when you could do the job just as well with a sponge.

■ In the home, use only durable dishware, utensils, and glassware. There is no need to eat regularly off disposable plates; furthermore it is expensive to do so.

■ For picnics and receptions, disposables have become standard. Throw a party without them; show yourself that it can be done.

■ Should you decide that paper and plastics are unavoidable, at least choose the lesser of the evils. Noncoated paper decomposes and burns more readily than plastic-coated paper or plastics. If you wash and reuse them, the more durable plastic glasses might be worthy of an exception to the no-plastics rule.

■ Use paper straws instead of plastic ones, or don't use straws at all.

■ Buy thumb tacks in boxes, not mounted on thick cardboard that is then encased in plastic.

■ To paraphrase a television advertisement, if two-ply is two trees, three-ply is three trees. Buy single-ply, noncolored toilet paper. The dyes in colored papers unnecessarily pollute the water.

■ Boycott products that are overly packaged—such as individually wrapped slices of cheese, pieces of candy, and servings of lemonade mix that are then enclosed in a plastic bag or a box.

■ Buy in bulk to reduce the proportion of packaging to contents.

■ Fancy packaging is meant to turn you on. If you care

about your environment, fancy packaging should turn you off.

▪ Follow some of the suggestions outlined in Chapter 9 to reduce your consumption of packaging.

▪ Share a magazine subscription with a friend and donate your used copies to a hospital or another institution that can use them. Terminate subscriptions to those publications that you never get around to reading. Read magazines and newspapers in the library.

▪ Do something to stop junk mail. Ask that your name be taken off the mailing lists. As a last defense, complain to the Post Office on the grounds that junk mail is "ecologically obscene."

▪ Buy quality. In the long run you will save money and reduce the amount of obsolete junk you have to toss out.

▪ Don't discard anything that can be fixed. Either fix it yourself, take it to a repairman, or donate it to someone who can have it fixed.

PROMOTE RECYCLING IN YOUR HOUSEHOLD

There are a large number of things you can recycle in your own household. Put some of your "waste" to use.

▪ There is no reason to buy plastic refuse bags or paper towels for dusting at the same time that you discard perfectly usable paper bags and old clothing that could be used as dusters.

▪ Reuse envelopes. Make use of both sides of paper.

▪ Return coat hangers to the cleaner instead of throwing them away.

▪ Turn a large tin can into a fire chimney for your charcoal grill. It's an inexpensive, non-polluting alternative to electrical starters and starter fluids. Simply cut both ends out of the can, punch some holes in the sides around the bottom for air vents, crumple up some newspaper in the bottom, fill the chimney with charcoal, and light. Once the coals are glowing, the chimney can be removed with a coathanger.

■ Fashion your own Christmas decorations out of bits of metal and paper you can find around the house.

■ Make use of kitchen scraps and leftovers. Boil beef and chicken bones to make soup stock. Skim off the fat and add leftover vegetables and rice and you will have an appetizing alternative to canned soups.

■ Make your own gravies from meat juices, rather than using packaged mixes.

■ Don't throw away beet greens; they can be prepared like spinach. Similarly, other vegetable greens, stalks, and seeds can be cooked and eaten.

■ Recycle your kitchen wastes, lawn clippings, leaves, and other decomposable organic matter by putting them in a compost pile. Consult Chapter 4. The compost is excellent fertilizer.

■ When your child outgrows his clothes or his toys, pass them on to a friend or relative who can use them or donate them to a charity.

■ Consider buying used goods. Not everything has to be new.

Despite your best efforts, you will not be able to eliminate entirely your contribution to the municipal trash load. Thus, your second objective should be to make disposal of your share as easy as possible. You can do this in several ways.

First, try to stay clear of those materials that are difficult to dispose of. Consult Table 32 in Chapter 9 for a general ranking of the desirability and undesirability of various types of packaging. Plastics, especially PVC, aluminum foils, and composite materials that combine two or more materials in the same package are worthy of a repeat warning. Unfortunately, all three of these materials are being used more and more.

About 90 million pounds of polyvinyl chloride stretch and shrink films are used per year, mostly in wrapping fresh meats and produce, and polyvinylidene chloride films (Saran) account for another 22 million pounds. In addition, PVC is used to make both the milk-white and clear plastic containers that are used to sell a wide variety of liquids. When incinerated these plastics produce hydrochloric acid aerosols that can destroy the metal interior of an incinerator. This is an unavoidable problem whenever trash containing PVC is burned.

Aluminum foils are undesirable because they don't degrade, because the aluminum that goes into them is expensive, and because the foil is unreclaimable, for it cannot be separated from the rest of the garbage by any method of mechanical segregation that has been devised to date. The same problem of separation exists with any composite materials.

From an ecological or resource-saving point of view, the only sensible method of disposing of waste involves recycling. But most recycling techniques that are available today need pure materials. Newsprint should be separated from other types of paper; steel should be free of tin, lead and copper; aluminum should be free of other metals; and glass should be free of metals. Thus, the problem with recycling materials from municipal trash collections is primarily one of segregating the different materials.

Most of the recycling that does take place today relies on industrial and commercial sources that can provide large quantities of such homogeneous materials. According to the National Association of Secondary Material Industries, Inc., such material accounts for 30% of the raw material supply of aluminum, 45% for copper and brass, 52% for lead, 20% for zinc, and 25% for paper stock. Thus, recycling is significant today.

But historically, recycling has been even more significant. During World War II almost 60% of the paper was recycled. Domestic sources of recyclable materials were important. Tin cans, rags, and paper were all collected. But today the detinning plants have all closed down and steel "tin" cans are less valuable as scrap. And the once-flourishing rag business has diminished with the advent of synthetic textiles.

The growth in environmental awareness, however, is contributing to a renewed interest in the recycling business. In four areas—newsprint, aluminum cans, steel cans, and glass—new opportunities appear to be opening for recycling of home-generated wastes.

Your cooperation is vital to making such efforts work. As you can see from Table 16, municipal refuse is far from homogeneous. It simply is not feasible to separate all of the different materials into different piles once they have been mixed together. Decide which materials you want to recycle and then segregate them at home from the rest of your trash. Most of the potentially smelly stuff will go to the compost pile. The newspapers can be accumulated in a stack, magazines in another, cardboard in yet another. Non-returnable glass should first be cleaned, then smashed into cullet to reduce the volume, then stored. If you use lots of cans, they should be rinsed out, flattened, and stored. If you separate the recyclable materials in this way, storage will be no problem because the trash is clean.

Before you accumulate a lot of material, you should line up a market for your collection. Investigate some of the leads listed on page 129. Find out whether any of the service groups, the Scouts, or ecology groups in your area has active recycling programs. Unless you combine your materials with your neighbors', it will take a fairly

TABLE 16. COMPOSITION OF REPRESENTATIVE MUNICIPAL REFUSE

Item		Per Cent By Weight
Corrugated paper boxes		25.70
Newspapers		10.34
Magazine paper		7.47
Brown paper		6.13
Mail		3.02
Paper food cartons		2.27
Tissue paper		2.18
Plastic coated paper and wax paper		1.68
	Subtotal	58.79
Vegetable and fruit wastes		4.20
Meat scraps (cooked) and fried fats		5.04
	Subtotal	9.24
Wood		2.52
Ripe tree leaves, flower garden plants, evergreens, and lawn grass (green)		7.56
	Subtotal	10.08
Metal		7.52
Glass, Ceramics, ash		8.49
Miscellaneous: Plastics, rags, leather and rubber goods, paints and oils, parts and dirt		5.88
		100.00

Source: (*Nation's Cities*, September, 1969)

long time to accumulate a very large quantity. If you can't find an active program, start one yourself. It is also a good way to raise some money for a worthy cause wherever volunteer labor is available.

Paper. Most paper products can be recycled. The easiest to handle is generally newsprint, in part because there is so much of it—it makes up about 10% of the total load of trash. A copy of the Sunday *New York Times* alone weighs five to six pounds. A 30-inch stack of newspapers, folded to half-page size as you buy them, weighs 100 pounds. Since a ton of newsprint represents pulp from about 17 trees, recycling a stack of newspapers about 36 inches high saves one tree. Recycling a ton of newsprint also eliminates a major portion of the pollution associated with producing new pulp. For the sulphite pulping process, this pollution includes 275 pounds of sulfur, 350 pounds of limestone, 60,000 gallons of water, 9,000 pounds of steam, and 225 kilowatt-hours of electricity, per ton of unbleached pulp.

The price for used newsprint averages about $8 a ton (in the Boston area) or less, and varies somewhat from that elsewhere. Most of the reused newsprint goes to make cheap cardboard, but some—about 365,000 tons in 1969 —is made into fresh newsprint. The leader in the field has been the Garden State Paper Company of Garfield, New Jersey, and there are plants in Garfield, Alsip, Illinois and Pomona, California. Recycled newsprint has been used regularly by the *Newark Evening News* and experimentally by others, most notably the *San Francisco Examiner*.

Corrugated cardboard also has a ready market. Check with the waste paper dealers in your area. You may be able to sell magazines and even mixed paper if it is not coated and is free of plastics.

Metals. There is usually a ready market for non-ferrous metals such as copper, lead, zinc, and aluminum. The metal you are likely to accumulate around the home is largely in the form of cans, primarily "tin" and aluminum. The tin cans are actually steel, and unfortunately, the tin coating and lead solder so contaminate the steel that its scrap value is reduced, but in some areas there is still a market. If detinning plants were reopened, this situation might change.

Beer and soft drink cans are usually made from steel or aluminum, sometimes steel with an aluminum pop-top lid. Both types have been recycled successfully. There is a market for aluminum cans—the ones with seamless moulded bottoms—in some areas. A recycling program was started in Los Angeles by Reynolds Aluminum. At half a cent per can and with only one reclamation center for all of Los Angeles, the program recycles an estimated 2 percent of the aluminum cans being distributed in that area. Certainly it would do a lot better if there were more collection centers. The program is being expanded to include Miami, Houston, New York, San Francisco, and the Pacific Northwest. Kaiser Aluminum and Chemical Corporation recently started a program in San Francisco, and arrangements are also being worked out with breweries that use cans.

Recycling of aluminum is doubly important, since the manufacture of the metal uses about 10 kilowatt-hours of electric power per pound. Remelting used metal is much less expensive in terms of energy. Also, aluminum cans have the property of being almost indestructible when they are discarded as litter. Unlike steel cans, they don't rust. Thus, discarded aluminum becomes a permanent pollutant.

Glass. Glass has a ready market for recycling because the crushed glass cullet can be used in glass manufacture to speed up the melting of the virgin silica. To be used for this purpose the cullet must be clean. Thus, when saving glass for recycling, you should rinse out the container, soak off any paper labels, and remove any metal such as the lid or the ring of metal around the top left by twist-off bottle caps. Separate the bottles by color. You can reduce the amount of storage space required by breaking the bottles.

A ton of glass cullet requires 3252 non-returnable soft drink bottles or 4228 beer bottles. The overall average for glass containers is 3610 per ton.

In June 1970 the Glass Container Manufacturers Institute (GCMI) announced a major recycling program for glass bottles. They have set up a network of redemption centers around the country (see Table 17). In Los Angeles their pilot project paid half a cent per bottle or a penny a pound, and the program has achieved a weekly redemption rate of half a million bottles. The stated goal of the national program is to salvage 11 billion bottles a year to meet 30 percent of the glass industry's raw material requirements. A state by state list of redemption centers is provided at the end of this chapter.

As praiseworthy as this and other recycling projects are, the most ecologically sound policy for you to follow is still one which minimizes use of all materials, whether recyclable or not. Never buy one-way bottles or cans or too many newspapers simply because they *can* be recycled. Returnable bottles don't have to be remelted and remade into new bottles; all they need is a good washing. For this reason they are cheaper; switching all soft drink and beer sales to returnable bottles would save an estimated total of $1½ billion dollars or $25 a year per family. Therefore, use returnable bottles and return them. Recycle only those that cannot be reused. Try to find a market for your large gallon jugs and wine bottles without smashing them for cullet.

At the same time that the GCMI is promoting recycling of their *non-returnable* bottles, they have been actively working against bans on sales of disposable containers that have been proposed in Madison, Wisconsin and elsewhere. In addition, they are spending $7½ million in 1970 to promote the use of one-way bottles (see below). From their point of view, everything hangs together. The rate at which glass containers are produced by manufacturers must continue to increase. But from the ecological point of view, their policy is schizophrenic—recycle, but make recycling even more necessary. The rational approach is to take the returnable bottle program that worked successfully in the past and try to make it work again now.

A returnable bottle used to make about 50 round trips

on the average. Today the figure is more like 15, and it gets as low as 4 in some cities. Do whatever you can to boost the average.

THE RHYTHM OF 'NO RETURN'

"Youth is 'the most important and dynamic' segment of the $4.5 billion soft drink market and the Glass Container Manufacturers Institute is making a pitch to teensters in their own rhythm. GCMI's ad agency, Benton & Bowles, has put together a rock music group, Soda Pop and the One-Way Bottles, to promote the use of no return soft drink bottles.

"The Institute will spend $7,500,000 in 1970 on the promotion. Besides saturation coverage in radio and TV network and spot commercials, the program will include two TV spectaculars as well as supermarket promotions featuring record albums of the One-Way Bottles as premiums.

"Paced in electronically amplified vibrations, the message is loud if not clear. It suggests almost subliminally that one-way bottles are better because they can be recapped and need not be returned. The glass folks claim the program is 'the largest single coordinated promotional effort ever undertaken on behalf of any consumer package."

—*Investor's Reader,* January 1, 1970

Cloth. Usable or reparable clothing should be sold or given away. Don't destroy good cloth. Worn-out clothing can be made into dusters, and old wool can be recycled to make fine-grade paper, but most of the synthetic fibers that are common today cannot be used for the latter purpose. If you cannot find a rag dealer, your cleaner may be able to direct you to one.

Marketing recycled items

To find a market for your paper, cans, glass, or other junk, try the following.

■ Look in the yellow pages of your telephone directory under:

Clothing—Secondhand	Aluminum
Junk	Bottles
Paper Stock—Waste	Boxes
Scrap Metals	Cans
Scrap Rubber	Cardboard
Secondhand Stores	Metals
Surplus & Salvage Merchandise	Rags
Waste	Steel

■ Contact local offices of:

> Aluminum companies
> Breweries
> Glass container manufacturers
> Soft drink bottling companies
> Steel companies
> Supermarket chains

■ Inquire of your local service organizations, the Scouts, and ecology action groups.

■ Call the Salvation Army.

WASTE THAT ISN'T REFUSE

Not all wastes are solid wastes and not all solid wastes are dealt with as trash. We flush a lot of waste down our toilets and sinks into the water system and forget about it in the same way we do the trash that the garbage man hauls away. We shouldn't. In addition, we send a lot of garbage into the air when we burn leaves in the fall or when we burn home refuse. Again we shouldn't. Observe the following rules.

■ Don't flush any waste into the water system that should stay on the land. You shouldn't use a kitchen food waste disposal. Compost your garbage instead.

■ Use non-phosphate, biodegradable detergents and cleaning agents.

■ Don't burn leaves; they should be composted and returned to the soil as fertilizer.

■ Refrain from open burning. It has been outlawed in many communities because of its contribution to air pollution.

WASTE MACHINES

The food waste disposal unit is only one of a variety of machines that are being promoted as solutions to waste disposal problems. The home incinerator is another. Both gas and electric model incinerators are available for between $120 to $200. Before you rush out and buy one, ask some questions. Does the incinerator live up to its smokeless, odorless claims? How much adjustment and repair will be needed to keep it operating properly? How does it handle PVC plastics and Saran? How much fuel does it use? Do you really need it? Incineration is ecologically less preferable than direct recycling or composting. If you live as you should, there won't be much waste to burn. If your municipal refuse disposal system works the way it should, there is no problem. If it doesn't, your $200 would probably do more to clean up pollution if it were in the form of a donation to an organization that is working on the solid waste problem in your area.

The home compacting unit is a new entry. Whirlpool is planning to introduce its Trash Masher in June 1970, for about $240. The unit reduces household trash into plastic-enclosed, compacted, disinfected blocks 12″ x 16″ x 16″ weighing 20 to 30 pounds. What is supposed to be done with the blocks is unclear. While compacting is an idea with some merit, locking up potentially valuable materials in compressed blocks is certainly a step in the wrong direction. If the Trash Masher is simply used to reduce the visible size of the waste disposal problem, it is no good. If it is used to compact already-segregated materials to reduce shipping bulk, then it might make sense.

LITTER

Don't litter. It's as simple as that. No one appreciates litter on the landscape. Keep America Beautiful, Inc., has estimated that $28 million was spent in 1967 collecting litter from the nation's primary highways. Show your respect for the land by making sure that you make no contribution to the litter that despoils it.

- Carry a litter bag in your car and use it.
- Make sure that trash cannot escape from your garbage cans, even on a windy day.
- Never dump trash illegally; report any violations of no-dumping areas that you see.
- Be willing to pick up other people's litter. If you have the courage, retrieve litter and return it to the litterbug on the spot. He may have "forgotten."
- Participate in clean-up campaigns and help to organize them.

TABLE 17.   NATIONAL BOTTLE REDEMPTION PROGRAM
CULLET COLLECTION CENTERS

STATE	COMPANY/PLANT/ADDRESS/TELEPHONE
Alabama	Brockway Glass Co. 3480 Lower Wetumpka Road Montgomery, Alabama 36110 205 265-0731
California	Anchor Hocking Corporation Plant #10 4855 E. 52nd Place Los Angeles, California 90022 213 581-7111
	Kerr Glass Mfg. Co. 1221 E. St., Andrews Place Santa Ana, California 714 545-0441
	Ball Corporation 4000 North Arden Drive El Monte, California 213 448-9831
	Brockway Glass Co. 1331 East Philadelphia St. Pomona, California 714 628-6081
	Latchford Glass Company 7537 Marbrisa Aven. Huntington Park, California 213 LU 7-7221
	Owens-Illinois, Inc. P.O. Box 3818 Term. Annex Los Angeles, California 90054 213 587-3281
	Owens-Illinois, Inc. P.O. Box 1019 Oakland, California 94604 415 532-7373

STATE	COMPANY/PLANT/ADDRESS/TELEPHONE
	Anchor Hocking Corporation Plant #4 1940 Fairway Drive San Leandro, California 415 357-6060
	Thatcher Glass Mfg. Co. Div. of Dart Industries Inc. 25655 Springbrook Road Saugus, California 91350 885 259-4400
	Anchor Hocking Corporation Plant #8 8653 Atlantic Avenue South Gate, California 90281
	Owens-Illinois, Inc. P.O. Box 30 Tracy, California 95376 209 835-5701
	Glass Container Corp. 2301 East 37th St. Vernon, California 213 582-5221
	Brockway Glass Co. 8717 G Street Oakland, California 94621 415 632-7250
	Glass Containers Corp. 4th & O Sts. Antioch, California 94509 415 757-0500
	Glass Containers Corp. 35 West A Street Hayward, California 94501 415 581-8816
Connecticut	Glass Containers Corp. Dayville, Connecticut 06241 203 774-9639
Florida	Anchor Hocking Corporation Plant #7 2121 Huron Street Jacksonville, Florida 32203 904 786-1010
	Owens-Illinois, Inc. P.O. Box 850 Lakeland, Florida 33802 813 683-5914
	Thatcher Glass Mfg. Co. 11316 North 46th Tampa, Florida 33612 813 971-8020
Georgia	Owens-Illinois, Inc. 3107 Sylvan Road Hapeville, Georgia 30054 404 766-2761
	Glass Containers Corp. 5158 Barnette Road Forest Park, Georgia 30050 404 366-7020
Illinois	Owens-Illinois, Inc. 1625 East Broadway Alton, Illinois 69002 618 465-3551
	Metro Glass Div. of Kraftco Corp. 138th St. & Cottage Grove Ave. Dolton, Illinois 60419 312-468-7800

STATE	COMPANY/PLANT/ADDRESS/TELEPHONE
	Obear-Nester Glass Company Div. of Indian Head Inc. East St. Louis, Illinois 62205 618 271-1491
	Anchor Hocking Corporation Plant #16 1955 Delaney Road Gurnee, Illinois 60031 312 244-1000
	Owens-Illinois, Inc. 901 N. Shabbona Street Streator, Illinois 61364 815 672-3141
	Ball Corporation 1200 East Town Line Road Mundelein, Illinois 60060 312 566-0600
	Thatcher Glass Mfg. Co. N. Walnut Street Streator, Illinois 61364 815 672-2951
Indiana	Kerr Glass Mfg. Corp. Packaging Products Division Dunkirk, Indiana 47336 317 768-5101
	Thatcher Glass Mfg. Co. Ridge Road Lawrenceburg, Indiana 812 537-1655
	Brockway Glass Co. Lapel, Indiana 46051 317 534-3121
	Glass Containers Corp. Box 110 Gas City, Indiana 46933 317 674-3351
	Glass Containers Corp. 1310 South Keystone Ave. Indianapolis, Indiana 46207 317 786-2211
	Owens-Illinois, Inc. 506 S. First St. Gas City, Indiana 46933 317 674-2201
	Foster-Forbes Glass Co. East Charles St. Marion, Indiana 46952 317 664-1251
	Anchor Hocking Corporation Plant #3 603 East North Street Winchester, Indiana 47394 317-46101 (as is)
Louisiana	Owens-Illinois, Inc. P.O. Box 26305 New Orleans, Louisiana 70126 504 241-3650
Maryland	Carr-Lowrey Glass Co. Div. of Anchor Hocking Corp. Plant #19 2201 Kloman Street Baltimore, Maryland 21231 301 752-5460
	Glass Containers Corp. Fort Ave. & Lawrence St. Baltimore, Maryland 21230 301 752-0700

STATE	COMPANY/PLANT/ADDRESS/TELEPHONE

Maryland Glass Corporation
Sub. of Chattanooga Glass Co.
2147 Wicomico Street
Baltimore, Maryland 21230
   301 837-3700

Michigan   Owens-Illinois, Inc.
P.O. Box 220
Charlotte, Michigan 48813
   517 543-1400

Minnesota   Brockway Glass Co.
Box 44
Rosemount, Minnesota 55068

Mississippi   Gulfport Glass Corporation, The
Sub. of Chattanooga Glass Co.
P.O. Box 2365
Gulfport, Mississippi 39208
   601 863-2474

Glass Containers Corp.
Fannin Road
Jackson, Mississippi 39208
   601 939-1771

New Jersey   Owens-Illinois, Inc.
P.O. Box 10
Bridgeton, New Jersey 08302
   609 461-6800

Brockway Glass Co.
P.O. Box 550
Freehold, New Jersey
   201 462-6500

Metro Glass
Div. of Kraftco Corporation
1 Minue Street
Carteret, New Jersey 07008
   201 969-1400

Metro Glass
Div. of Kraftco Corporation
107 West Side Avenue
Jersey City, New Jersey 07303
   201 434-5000

Thatcher Glass Mfg. Co.
Washington Avenue
Wharton, New Jersey
   201 461-2111

Kerr Glass Mfg. Corp.
Packaging Products Division
P.O. Box 150
Milleville, New Jersey 08332
   609 825-5000

Owens-Illinois, Inc.
P.O. Box 891
No. Bergen, New Jersey 07047
   201 869-3400

Anchor Hocking Corporation
Plant #6
83 Griffith Street
Salem, New Jersey 08079
   609 935-4000

New York   Owens-Illinois, Inc.
P.O. Box 260
Brockport, New York
   716 637-3181

Glenshaw Glass Co.
Glenshaw Street
Orangeburg, New York 10962
   914 359-2300

STATE	COMPANY/PLANT/ADDRESS/TELEPHONE
	Thatcher Glass Mfg. Co. North Walnut Street Elmira, New York 607 RE 4-7161
North Carolina	Ball Corporation 1856 Hendersonville Road Asheville, North Carolina 28803 704 274-1661
Ohio	Chattanooga Glass Company P.O. Box 829 Mt. Vernon, Ohio 43050 614 397-5161
	Brockway Glass Co. 1937 Bridge Avenue Zanesville, Ohio 43701 614 452-7581
Oklahoma	Brockway Glass Co. Muskogee, Oklahoma 74402 918 682-6621
	Ball Corporation Okmulgee, Oklahoma 74447 918 765-5990
	Liberty Glass Company North Mission Road Sapulpa, Oklahoma 74066 918 BA 4-1440
	Brockway Glass Co. 300 East 4th Street Ada, Oklahoma 74820 405 332-0415
Oregon	Owens-Illinois, Inc. P.O. Box 20067 Portland, Oregon 97220 503 254-7331
Pennsylvania	Owens-Illinois, Inc. P.O. Box 150 Clarion, Pennsylvania 16214 814 226-7600
	Glass Containers Corp. Parker, Pennsylvania 412 399-2441
	Glass Containers Corp. Marienville, Pa. 16239 814 927-6666
	Glass Containers Corp. Knox, Pa. 16232 814 797-1111
	Pierce Glass Company Div. of Indian Head Port Alleghany, Pa. 814 642-2521
	Anchor Hocking Corp. Plant #5 1926 Baldridge St. So. Connellsville, Pa. 412 628-4000
	Brockway Glass Co. Brockway, Pa. 15824 814 216-6452
	Brockway Glass Co. Crenshaw, Pa. 15830 814 261-5389
	Brockway Glass Co. Wylie Avenue & Connecting Railroad Washington, Pa. 15301 412 222-9000

STATE	COMPANY/PLANT/ADDRESS/TELEPHONE
	Brockway Glass Co. 331 South Main St. Washington, Pa. 15301 412 225-2400
	Glenshaw Glass Co. William Flynn Highway Glenshaw, Pa. 412 961-0200
	Anchor Hocking Corp. Plant #15 1840 Baldridge St. So. Connellsville, Pa. 412 628-4000
	Metro Glass Div of Kraftco Corp. 41 Detroit Avenue Washington, Pa. 15301 412 225-7500
South Carolina	Laurens Glass Company Div of Indian Head Inc. P.O. Box 9 Laurens, S. C. 29360 803 984-2541
Tennessee	Chattanooga Glass Co. 400 West 45th St. Chattanooga, Tenn. 37410
Texas	Chattanooga Glass Company P.O. Box 956 Corsicana, Texas 75110 214 874-7437
	Anchor Hocking Corp. Plant #18 4202 Fidelity St. Houston, Texas 77029 713 672-0591
	Owens-Illinois, Inc. P.O. Box 1789 Waco, Texas 76703 817 754-4611
	Glass Containers Corp. Palestine, Texas 75801 214 729-2141
	Kerr Glass Mfg. Corporation Packaging Products Division P.O. Box 677 Waxahachie, Texas 75165 214 WE 7-3430
Washington	Northwestern Glass Company Div. of Indian Head Inc. 5801 East Marginal Way South Seattle, Washington 98134 206 762-0660
West Virginia	Owens-Illinois, Inc. P.O. Box 592 Fairmont, West Virginia 26554 304 363-8100
	Owens-Illinois, Inc. P.O. Box 640-670 Huntington, West Virginia 304 529-7191
	Brockway Glass Co. Deluth Glass Division Parkersburg, West Virginia 26101 304 295-4511
Wisconsin	Foster-Forbes Glass Co. Burlington, Wisconsin 414 763-9161

8. Home Environmental Hazards

Hazards have always been a part of man's world. It would be folly to believe that we will ever reach a time when this will not be the case. The heart of the situation is that as man gains knowledge of how the world works, he is driven by an inborn curiosity to apply that knowledge in new ways. New applications breed new hazards, and the cycle is constantly renewed. At the same time, man's instinct for survival drives him to find ways to eliminate the hazards or to live with them.

The explosive growth of technology has recreated our world. We are still trying to learn how to live with our enormous supplies of power, our rapid transportation and communication, and the thousands of chemical tools that the technologists have placed in our hands.

The purpose of this chapter is to look at a selected few of the environmental hazards that originate in the home or that must be dealt with there. The same ecological reasoning and common sense that are applied to these problems should be applied to any similar problem. If environment is viewed as meaning "everything that surrounds us," any problem becomes an environmental problem. Indeed, no consumer choice should be made without some consideration of its broader impact.

NOISE POLLUTION

The problem

Noise is pollution. It is an agent that decreases property values, creates physical damage, impairs hearing, impedes efficiency, and threatens the sanity of modern man.

■ Over the past thirty years, background noise has been increasing at the rate of one decible per year. In cities like New York, noise levels commonly exceed the 80 decibel level considered dangerous.

■ The World Health Organization has estimated that noise in working environments causes a yearly loss of $4 billion in the U.S., due to lowered efficiency and increased errors resulting.

■ Studies with relatively noise-free cultures in the Sudan have indicated that the normal loss of hearing that starts in U.S. men at 32 and in women at 37 may be caused by high general noise levels rather than by aging.

■ "Hard-rock" music reaches 115 decibels in noise intensity. This causes damage to hearing and can bring on deafness at an early age.

■ Combat training causes such widespread hearing loss that about half of the soldiers who undergo it would be barred from combat, were they recruits. The V.A. pays 60,000 veterans about $3.3 million per month for hearing impairments.

■ In the U.S., 11 million adults and 3 million children suffer from some hearing loss.

■ Exposing the mother to excessive noise can harm the unborn fetus.

■ Noise contributes to and aggravates all tension-related diseases; headaches, stomach ulcers, neuroses, mental illness, allergies—even cardiovascular and circulatory diseases.

■ Wild animals react adversely to invasion of their habitat by snowmobiles and aircraft overflights.

■ Sonic booms from faster-than-sound airplanes crack plaster, break windows, and damage buildings. A program of 49 test flights over Chicago in 1965 produced 6000 complaints, half that many damage claims, and a total of $114,763 actually paid in damages. It has been estimated that a fleet of 150 supersonic transports in normal operation could inflict $1 million of physical damage each day.

Measuring noise

The unit of noise is the decibel (db). Zero decibels is at the threshold of hearing. A decibel scale is defined by the mathematical expression $10 \log_{10} P/P_0$. This means that doubling the sound power (P) raises the decibel level of the noise 3 db; increasing by a factor of 4 (an additional factor of 2) raises it 6 db; by 8, 9db, and so forth.

On the decibel scale a few levels are especially significant. Somewhere around 180 db is the lethal level. Rats exposed to 150 db first turn homosexual and cannibalistic and eventually are killed by heart failure. Short exposure to 150 db can permanently damage the human ear. The threshold of pain is around 120 db. Short exposure to between 100 and 125 db can cause temporary deafness, and long-term exposure to anything over 80 db invites hearing loss.

TABLE 18. COMMON NOISE LEVELS

The threshold of hearing	0 db
The danger level	80 db
The threshold of pain	120 db
The lethal level	180 db
Jet aircraft at 200 feet	150 db
Pneumatic riveter, air raid siren	130 db
A "hard-rock" band	115 db
Power mower, accelerating motorcycle	110 db
Food blender (2 to 4 feet away)	100 db
Subway train	100 db
Heavy city traffic	90 db
Diesel trucks at 50 feet	68–99 db
Passenger cars at 50 feet	65–86 db
Loud shout at 1 foot	88 db
Normal conversation	60–70 db
Limit for phone conversation	60 db
Quiet street, average urban interior	50 db
Quiet room, residential area at night	40 db
Tick of watch at 2 feet	30 db
Whisper	20 db
Leaves rustling in the wind	10 db

Source: The primary source for this table is "Noise Pollution: an Introduction to the Problem and an Outline for Future Legal Research," James L. Hildebrand in *The Columbia Law Review*, Vol. 70, page 652 (April 1970).

Combating noise

Minimize noise at the source. Table 18 summarizes a variety of commonly experienced sounds. You meet some of them at work, in your home, out of doors, and in transit. You have control over many of them, especially those in the home. Do what you can to stop this noise at its source.

■ The kitchen, TV room, and play room are the noise centers of the home. Kitchen appliances such as waste disposals, blenders, and dishwashers can raise the noise level to over 100 decibels. Noise is one more reason for minimizing your use of these machines. To avoid noise and for other reasons, food waste disposers should not be used at all.

■ Noise-test any appliance before you buy it. Manufacturers have varying degrees of success in quieting their products. In general, the more powerful the machine, the more noisy it is likely to be.

■ An appliance can be made less noisy by placing it on a sound-absorbent pad.

■ The television set introduces an enormous amount of noise into the home. Keep it under control.

■ Allegations have been made that consumers will not buy vacuum cleaners that do not *sound* powerful. It is up to you to prove this is not so. The Southcoat Company is reportedly testing a vacuum cleaner for dentists' offices that is 50 times more powerful than the home cleaner, but is quieter.

■ There is a reasonable limit on power for music systems. The acoustic power output of a full orchestra seldom rises above 10 watts. Unless you aspire to follow Beethoven into deafness, there isn't much reason to equip your living room with hundreds of watts of audio power.

■ If you want to take up an instrument, pick one that doesn't have a plug and an amplifier attached.

■ Turn the ring on your telephone down. There is usually a lever on the bottom. Ask the telephone company about some of the less-noisy alerting devices that can be substituted for the loud ring.

■ If you have a second phone installed, make it an extension so that you can unplug it.

■ Some heating systems are quieter than others. In general, forced air heat tends to produce a blower noise, and the ducts conduct noise well. Water pipes can gurgle, steam pipes knock, and electric resistance heaters crackle. Don't install an electric heating system just because it is supposed to be cleaner or quieter. Depending on which systems you compare, electric heat may actually be noisier. It is a cinch that generating the heat with electricity is more costly to the environment, if not to your wallet.

■ Plumbing can also be a source of noise and a means for transmitting it from apartment to apartment. Plastic plumbing has noise-insulating advantages. A study commissioned by the Cast Iron Soil Pipe Institute has determined that cast iron pipes with neoprene couplings transmit the least noise and vibration, apparently because of the mass of the iron and the insulation of the neoprene.

■ Garbage-can noise can be bothersome, especially if the garbage collector comes early in the morning. Quiet steel cans and plastic ones can be bought. Because of the problem of solid waste disposal, non-biodegradable plastic bags, though quiet, are less desirable. Of course, reducing household trash will have the effect of reducing the number of cans you must use.

■ Buy a quiet lawn mower. Some power mowers have motors strong enough to drive a car. If your lawn is small enough, you should find a hand-propelled, reel mower entirely adequate and relatively quiet.

■ Squeaky machinery can often be cured with a little bit of oil.

Defend your home against noise. Drowning out noise with noise may work, but only to a point, for the 'perfume' noise can itself be too noisy. It makes more sense to take steps to reduce the effect of the unwanted noise by other means.

■ Inside the house, carpeting, acoustical ceiling tile, and draperies all deaden noises. Acoustical ceilings can absorb between 55 and 75 percent of the sound energy striking their surfaces.

■ Transmission of sound through interior walls can be inhibited by constructing the walls with a staggered stud design. Each side of the wall has an independent set of studs, with sound insulating blankets between. Such construction is, of course, more expensive. However, specially sound-conditioned houses, costing $600 to $800 more than equivalent unconditioned houses, sell better despite their higher price.

■ You can isolate noises by placing noisy appliances in separate rooms.

■ Insulating yourself from outside noise by caulking windows and weatherstripping doors also helps reduce fuel consumption in the winter. The extreme of this method of noise control, however, results in isolating yourself in a completely controlled habitat with air conditioning. The environmental cost of the power for the air conditioning alone is unacceptable. Work out a compromise that makes sense to you.

■ Out of doors, trees serve the same sound-absorbing function as drapes do indoors, while lawns are similar in effect to carpets. Asphalt driveways and concrete patios, on the other hand, cause noises to reverberate.

■ Noise falls off as the square of the distance. Thus, doubling the distance between you and the source diminishes the noise by a factor of four, or six db.

Control your contribution to the general noise level:

■ Respect your neighbors by controlling the level of noise that emanates from your home.

■ The air conditioner that is quiet from the inside is not necessarily quiet from the outside. Your neighbors have to put up with your noisy machine or you with theirs.

■ Keep your automobile muffler in good condition.

■ Use your automobile horn as sparingly as possible.

■ Don't accelerate unnecessarily; it can be noisy.

■ Avoid taking airplane flights that are scheduled to take off or leave in the middle of the night, when they disturb sleepers.

Work to control public sources of noise.

If the supersonic transport (SST) should ever become operational, boycott it. Even if flights are restricted to "non–populated" (by people) areas, the sonic boom will be damaging and offensive. Wild life and fish are adversely affected. The boom has also caused damage by precipitating landslides in the National Parks. Nor will ocean travelers appreciate it. Write the major airlines, telling them of your intention to boycott the SST and why.

Unfortunately, regulation of public noise is still in its infancy. Support noise ordinances and report violators. Much noise is avoidable. For example, construction equipment such as air compressors and jackhammers that produce lower levels of noise are available, and have been in use in Europe for some time.

RADIATION AND MICROWAVES

All of us are exposed to low levels of background radiation all of the time. It is as natural as rocks and sunlight, both of which deliver some of it to us. In high doses radiation is known to have bad effects and even a low dose over a long period of time is considered unhealthy. Although maximum "acceptable" levels have been set, there is a large body of scientific opinion which holds that the amount of damage is proportional to the dose and thus that the only "acceptable" level is the lowest achievable level.

The growth of nuclear technology since the mid-1940's has brought with it a worldwide increase in the background levels of radiation. This increase arises from fallout from atmospheric and underground nuclear testing, from small amounts of leakage permitted from nuclear power plants, and from the industry that produces nu-

clear fuels out of ores taken from the earth. You can do
essentially nothing to protect yourself from this background radiation except to agitate that testing cease and
that there be full disclosure of our knowledge about the
effects and safety of atomic energy, or our lack of that
knowledge. But the French and the Chinese, who are
both still testing in the atmosphere, will not listen. And
your own government has left regulation of nuclear energy to the Atomic Energy Commission, the body charged
with promoting the use of the same. If their plans reach
fruition, most of our electricity will be generated in atomic
power plants, our canals will be excavated using nuclear
explosives, and our natural gas will be freed from the
rocky depths by underground nuclear explosions. None
of these plans can be accomplished without some radioactive contamination.

You don't have to rely on the A.E.C. to bring radiation
into your home. You can do it yourself by buying a color
television set or a microwave oven. The type of radiation
is not precisely the same, but the potential in terms of
genetic damage, induction of tumors, and other harm to
living tissues is.

Color television

In 1967, General Electric discovered that 115,000 of
its color television sets were possibly emitting excessive
levels of X-radiation. The problem was with an insuffi-
ciently shielded component; a device that was required to
regulate the higher voltages needed by the color picture
tube. The problem with the G.E. sets was duly corrected,
but television sets that produce high levels of radiation
continued to be manufactured in significant numbers.

Two years after the G.E. incident, action was taken.
The Department of Health, Education, and Welfare set a
schedule dictating that all TV sets manufactured after
January 1, 1970 could emit no more than half a milli-
roentgen per hour, a limit commonly set in laboratories.
And so, is the public protected? Not really. Component

failure or maladjustment can put a set over the limit; a restriction to prohibit this will not go into effect until June 1, 1971. Furthermore, there are many old, potentially dangerous color sets in homes all over the country.

As a precaution against this radiation risk, the Surgeon General has suggested that viewers stay 6 to 10 feet from the set while viewing. Avoid the sides and rear as these areas are where the highest levels of leakage occur. Be especially careful with children. Games that allow a child to write on a plastic screen placed over the television tube have been sold. They should not be used with a color set.

Radiation levels can be controlled by proper design. Some models have relatively high radiation while others produce nothing measurable. Ask the dealer about radiation levels from any set you might consider buying. Do not be satisfied by an assurance that it meets federal standards, as many sets actually do better than that. You want the lowest level of radiation possible. Manufacturers should be required to list the actual levels measured on each model.

Devices have been marketed that are supposed to alert you when radiation levels from your home set get too high. They are fairly expensive (about $40) and have dubious value if they are only black boxes telling you something about what is coming out of another black box.

A comment about television. To dwell only on the radiation hazard from television sets would be to miss the significant impact this machine has had on the home environment. What role does the television play in your home? Does it rule you or do you rule it?

These questions are relevant to a book about protecting the environment because television has become such a central part of the way many people experience the environment. It is relevant to a book that is interested in consumer matters because television advertising has such a strong influence in shaping consumer decisions.

Consider what less television might do for your life style. You would have more time for:

                                                    play
    reading
                                             music
                        gardening
        sports   thinking
                       gourmet cooking
                                           recycling
        recreation
                                  love
                                           theater
                           discussion
    visiting
                      bicycling
                                           exercise
    experiencing the real world

    And less noise and advertising.
    Think about it.

Microwave ovens

Like the color television set, the microwave oven has
been identified as a potentially dangerous source of radiation. Use of microwave ovens, however, is much less
widespread. About 40,000 units are in home use and
another 60,000 in institutional or vending machine use.

Microwaves are electromagnetic radiation, like X-rays
and light, but of a different energy level. They are used
in ovens because they interact with molecules in foods,
transferring their energy to the tumbling motions of the
food molecules and creating heat. Microwaves cook a
roast, for example, by penetrating throughout the roast
instead of heating only from the surface inward. Thus
the meat cooks much faster than in a standard oven.

The problem with microwaves is that they do not make
a distinction between food and human flesh. A leaky
microwave oven can cook you. A standard of 10 milliwatts per square centimeter (mW/cm^2) has been set because this is considered to be the maximum amount of

heat that the body can dissipate under normal conditions of temperature and humidity.

Tests on ovens actually in use have repeatedly shown that a large proportion, typically one third of them, leak at levels above the 10 mW/cm² level. Damage to the viewing screen in the oven door can release vastly more than this. Some ovens tested actually leaked as much as several hundred milliwatts per square centimeter. Models that operate while the door is open by design or because of failure of an interlock system can expose the user to 700 mW/cm².

This situation is even more alarming given the concern over the validity of the 10 mW/cm² limit. Experiments have shown that 120 mW/cm² for thirty-five minutes will cause cataract formation in a rabbit's eye. There is a possibility of cumulative effects, which would mean that chronic exposure to much lower levels would be dangerous.

Considerable research has been conducted by Soviet scientists on the effects of even lower doses of microwave radiation than those mentioned above. Among the effects noted were changes in the nervous system and the composition of blood, low blood pressure and imbalance in hormone levels. Other work has uncovered genetic damage. The Russians have been disturbed enough by their findings that they have set the following standards:

0.01 mW/cm² full-day exposure
0.1   mW/cm² no more than 2 hours
1.0   mW/cm² no more than 15 to 20 minutes
                 (wearing goggles)

Although American authorities have not yet accepted the Soviet findings, American standards are being revised. In the May 22, 1970, issue of the *Federal Register,* new standards for microwave oven leakage were published by the Environmental Control Administration of H.E.W. The new standards call for no more than 1 mW/cm² from new ovens at 5 cm distance, (about 2 inches) and no more than 1 mW/cm² as the oven grows old. If the standards are implemented, the mandatory compliance date will be July 1, 1971. Thus, permissible levels will still exceed the least stringent Soviet standard by a factor of as much as five.

Microwave communications

Microwaves are also used for communications. Television transmission is by microwaves: one mile from the transmitter of an average station the field strength is about 0.1 mW/cm^2 and three miles away it's about 0.01 mW/cm^2, the Soviet limit for continuous exposure. Thus, the Soviet standards would interfere with American television transmission practices. Microwaves also are used to beam telephone conversations between relay stations and in airport radar.

Nuclear energy, color television, and microwave ovens are examples of what has been happening on the leading edge of technology as it relates to consumer matters. The hazard that this technology poses to man and his environment is in many ways subtle and not fully understood, for many of the effects are not immediate and tangible. The induction of a disease, the shortening of a life by several years, and the mutation in the eggs or sperm that one carries in one's body are real dangers even if their full expression doesn't come for five or ten years, or even for several generations.

CHEMICALS IN THE HOME

Hazardous chemicals are used in almost every household. Some of these chemical "helpers" are immediately injurious or toxic, while many others have effects that are expressed more subtly—as with radiation. Cleaning products, polishes and waxes, wax removers, oven cleaners, disinfectants, room fresheners, cosmetics, insecticides and other pesticides, and food additives all expose us to chemicals that can have deleterious effects on us if we do not take the appropriate precautions, and often even if we do.

We have seen in other chapters some of the hazards

and environmental problems associated with pesticides, food additives, and cosmetics. The story with respect to the other products mentioned above is very similar. Surveillance by the governmental regulatory agencies is just as poor, labeling information is frequently inadequate, and manufacturers show the same callous disregard for the safety of the users of their products.

The Federal Hazardous Substances Act requires that "hazardous substances" be labeled with an appropriate cautioning statement, precautionary measures that should be followed, and instruction for first aid or antidotes as appropriate. The Food and Drug Administration passes on whether labels for products comply with the requirements of the law. Thus, for many substances there is a warning.

A large part of the reason that there are so many accidental poisonings and injuries is that many people never read the labels or, if they do, they quickly forget or dismiss the warnings. This, in turn, is a result of the attitudes that advertising has engendered. Convenience, ease of use, pleasant odors, cleaning power or killing power (for bugs), and effectiveness are emphasized with no mention of risks at all.

An insecticide. A brief look at one product, an insecticide, is indicative of the problem. Johnson Wax's Raid Flying Insect Killer has been actively promoted as a safe way to get rid of noisome bugs. The advertisements, of course, say nothing about the possible dangers of using the product and, in fact, imply that it is safe by saying it contains no DDT. The front of the can prominently displays the statements:

CLEAN PLEASANT ODOR!
KILLS BUGS DEAD
NONTOXIC TO HUMANS AND PETS

and the directions read: "Close all doors and windows. Spray Raid up into the air with a sweeping motion, keeping about 3 feet from interior walls, fabrics, furniture, until room is filled with mist." The only warning reads "CAUTION: KEEP OUT OF REACH OF CHILDREN"; something found on almost any can, and there is a warning about the danger of puncturing or incinerating an aerosol container. The user is not warned to avoid inhaling the vapors or to minimize exposure, despite the presence of 1.00% piperonyl butoxide as a synergist. (See page 69.)

Polychlorinated biphenyls. Polychlorinated biphenyls provide another example of the sort of hazards that the home user of chemicals must face. Like DDT, PCBs are long-lived chlorinated hydrocarbons that have been found widely in the body fat of predaceous birds and fish and in human fat and milk. In large quantities they are known to be poisons, and in small quantities they are suspected of interfering with liver enzymes and affecting sex hormones.

Monsanto, the only American manufacturer of PCBs, has reportedly decided to restrict sales of the chemical "because of mounting evidence that it can induce birth defects in animals." According to a *New York Times* article (July 15, 1970), Monsanto launched a campaign several years ago to market PCBs under the trade name AROCLOR for use in such household products as floor waxes, outdoor paints, and caulking compounds. The product is used in a number of paints and adhesives, in asphalt, in hydraulic oil, as a water-resistant plasticizer, a lubricant in transformers, and (according to a USDA official) in at least eight different brands of insecticides now on the market.

The *Times* report referred to a statement by a Monsanto spokesman that publication of a list of all products now containing PCB would "serve no useful non-political purpose." Apparently warning consumers is not considered a useful purpose. Congressman William F. Ryan has asked for Department of Agriculture action and urged that any product containing PCBs be so labeled.

What should you do?

Rather than dwelling on the hazards of each of the different chemicals, this section will attempt to set forth the outlines of a strategy that will minimize the hazards and the adverse impact on the environment while achieving an acceptable approximation of what the chemical wonders are supposed to accomplish.

Handle chemical products with care. The first rule in this strategy is to handle chemical products with the care that they deserve. Strong alkalies such as lye, potassium and sodium hydroxides, and trisodium phosphate, and less-strong alkalies such as washing soda, ammonia, and borates are commonly used in grease-cutting cleaners. Strong acids such as hydrochloric and sulfuric acids and the weaker acids in vinegar and lemon juice are used to remove hard-water deposits and metal stains. Bleaches are added to household cleaners to oxidize stains away. *It is most unwise ever to mix such cleaners.* The resulting cocktail may produce a substance that could seriously injure you.

- Anything with a "Keep out of reach of children" warning really should be kept out of the reach of children. It is wise to *lock up* hazardous chemicals.

- The products should be kept in their original containers so that the label can be reread before each use. Ideally, such products should not be stored for a very long time.

- When scrubbing floors, walls, or windows with ammonia or when spraying a room, windows should be kept *open* to provide good ventilation in the room.

- Strong alkalies and acids should not be used without wearing protective gloves.

Minimize usage of harmful products. The best thing to do, however, is to try to minimize your use of the harmful products. For many of them, there are perfectly acceptable alternatives that cost much less and which place much smaller demands on the environment.

- Window cleaners are an example. A solution of one tablespoon of household ammonia in a quart of water does as good a job as aerosols that cost 50¢ and more.

Furthermore, the water and ammonia mixture can be used in a refillable, finger-pump squirt bottle which avoids the objectionable aerosol container.

■ Similarly, a damp cloth is adequate for most dusting jobs. The shiny surface that is considered fashionable now has not always been so. Cleanliness should be the object, not gloss. The cycle of waxing, dewaxing, and re-waxing is so unnecessary.

■ Soap and water are sufficient for many of the jobs for which strong disinfectants are now used.

■ Baking soda and washing soda are environmentally preferable to phosphate-containing all-purpose cleaners such as Ajax, Comet, and Dutch Cleanser; and do just as well in many cases.

■ Clean out your electric coffee percolator by brewing a couple of cups of baking soda solution.

■ Room fresheners cannot take out stale odors; they only cover them up. Instead of spraying more junk into the air, freshen the room by ventilating it. Open the windows, get rid of any sources of undesirable odors, and bring in a bouquet of flowers.

DETERGENT PHOSPHATES AND EUTROPHICATION

Synthetic detergents have been recognized as an environmental problem ever since their foam began turning our rivers into sudsy streams in the early 1960s. More recently, attention has been focused on the problem of phosphates in detergents bringing about the eutrophication of our lakes and rivers.

How detergents work

Supposedly, soap was first used by the early Romans, who discovered that the mixture of fat and ashes from animal sacrifices with a particular clay, called sapo clay, got the dirt out of clothing. For centuries, soap was made in the same way, by boiling lye and grease together to get the salt of natural long–chain fatty acids. During the 1940s, synthetic detergents, in which the soap was replaced by a functionally similar surfactant, were introduced.

Soap and surfactant molecules have two ends. The salt or ionic end interacts well with water, while the non–ionic end prefers to associate with oils and grease. In action, these molecules surround the water–insoluble dirt with their fatty, non–ionic ends, forming what is called a micelle, which makes the dirt soluble. The water–liking, ionic ends form the outer surface of the micelle.

Foam problems arose because manufacturers were using surfactants whose fatty end was composed of unnatural, branched-chain hydrocarbons. Bacteria that break down wastes do not have enzymes that can attack the branched molecules, so the non–biodegradable detergents accumulated in the environment. Fortunately, this problem had a relatively simple solution. The branched surfactants were modified so that the hydrocarbon, fatty ends were unbranched and therefore digestible by bacteria. This changeover was completed in 1965; today all commercial detergents are biodegradable.

What is eutrophication?

Below is described what happens to a body of water during the natural process called eutrophication. Normally, eutrophication happens very slowly, on a time scale of many tens of thousands of years, but since the appearance of technological man, the process has been accelerated enormously. An estimate has been made that Lake Erie has aged 15,000 years since 1920!

> Overstimulated, the waterplants grow to excess. Seasonally they die off and rot, either in place or after washing up on beaches, where they may pile up in thick mats. In the process of decay they exhaust the dissolved oxygen of the water and produce the rotten–egg stench of hydrogen sulfide. Simultaneously they release

their phosphorus content, to start the growth
cycle anew. The game fish die of oxygen defi-
ciency and are replaced, for a time, by rough
varieties. Intake filters for potable water become clogged, and boat propellers fouled, with
algae. The lake loses its value as a water supply, as an esthetic and recreational asset, and as
an avenue of commerce. Finally, the water itself
is displaced by the accumulated masses of living
and dead vegetation and their decay products,
and the lake becomes a bog, and, eventually,
dry land.

—*Report of the Subcommittee on Conservation
and Natural Resources,* Rep. Henry Reuss,
Chairman; Committee on Government Operations

What has caused this? Consider what the situation was
before man invented plumbing. The beasts which then
roamed the earth, and probably the men too, didn't search
for a stream when they needed to relieve themselves.
Their dung fertilized the soil. Microorganisms broke down
the dung, converting it into forms that plants could use.
The ecological cycle was intact—from plant to beast to
the soil and back to the plant.

The advent of modern plumbing and the flush toilet
broke the cycle as far as human waste was concerned.
Instead of going back into the soil, man's wastes went
into the most convenient body of water. Fortunately, water
can also absorb rather large quantities of nutrients. It
too contains microorganisms that break down the wastes
into forms that aquatic plants and algae can use. However, only a tiny fraction of the nutrients cycle back to
man by way of the fish he eats. The rest stays in the
water and eventually settles to the bottom.

Eutrophication is a probem when there is an excess
of *all* of the nutrients that algae and aquatic plants need
to grow. In healthy lakes and streams there is always at
least one vital nutrient that is present in a limiting low

concentration. When it gets used up, no more growth can take place. Usually the limiting factor is phosphorus.

Detergents and eutrophication

The figures vary but in general, municipal wastes contribute about 60 to 90 percent of the phosphorus to those bodies of water where eutrophication is a problem, and detergents account for about 50 to 70 percent of the municipal waste load.

Lake Ontario: 57% of P from municipal and industrial wastes
Lake Erie: 70% of P from municipal and industrial wastes
Potomac River: 90% of P from all waste water discharges

The proportion of phosphorus accounted for by detergents is nicely confirmed by comparison of the per capita contribution of phosphorus from human excrement in sewage (1.2 pounds of phosphorus each year by best estimates) with that from detergents (about 2 pounds).

The critical phosphorus concentration seems to be about 10 micrograms per liter at the beginning of the growing season. That two pounds of phosphorus from your detergents, if placed in 24 million gallons of water, will produce a concentration of 10 micrograms per liter. This amounts to 120,000 cubic yards of water or a polluted lake nine feet deep and 220 yards in diameter! One cup of Tide (77 grams), which contains 12.4% phosphorus, in a washing machine that uses a total of 45 gallons of water delivers a rinse with a phosphorus content of 56,000 micrograms per liter. ($\mu g/1$).

Algae growth is known to increase with increasing phosphorus levels. Thus, Lake Erie's condition has steadily worsened as the dissolved phosphorus levels escalated from $14\mu g/1$ in 1942 to $30\mu g/1$ in 1958 and $40\mu g/1$ in 1967.

The detergent manufacturers have alleged that phos-

phorus is not the real culprit, but their arguments can
be countered. Certainly, phosphorus *is* the problem in
the Great Lakes and the Potomac River. A defense of
phosphorus by L. E. Kuentzel of Wyandotte Chemicals
and a refutation (and indictment of phosphorus) by
Joseph Shapiro of the University of Minnesota are reprinted in the Reuss Committee hearings (pp. 246-256
and 284-287, respectively).

What can be done about eutrophication?

Fortunately, once the input of phosphates ceases, nature is able to start restoring the balance in lakes that are
deep enough for there is a natural removal of nutrients
as decaying matter falls to the bottom.

The only sensible approach, then, is to stop dumping
phosphates into our waterways. The detergent contribution can be stopped at two points. Predictably, the detergent manufacturers have pushed for removal of phosphates at the sewage treatment level. This, however, is
both expensive and, in the short run, ineffective, since
simple primary and secondary treatment removes very
little phosphate and since a large portion of the population is not hooked into treatment systems. The alternate
approach—to have the detergent manufacturers take phosphates out of their products—has the virtue of stopping
cold the use of over 487 million pounds (the 1967 figure)
of phosphorus. Furthermore, it can be implemented
quickly.

In the long run, however, the solution proposed by
the detergent manufacturers is correct. The ecologically
sound way to deal with the sewage "waste" problem is to
recognize that sewage is not waste but misplaced fertilizer.

How can you minimize your contribution to the problem?

Do you (1) presoak with half a cup of a high–phosphate
product, then (2) wash with 1½ cups of a phosphate–

built detergent, (3) adding, perhaps, some bleach, water conditioner, and fabric softener? DON'T!

The first thing you should do is to make up your own mind about how clean is clean and how white is white is clean. "Optical brighteners" that are used in most detergents merely absorb ultraviolet light and radiate it as visible. Because different cultures have different concepts of what is clean white, the brighteners are actually different from country to country. Our clean white has a bluish tint while that in South America is a bit reddish. Clearly, this "whiteness" has no effect on cleanliness or sanitation. The fetish has been carried too far.

Soap and soda. The ecologically approved solution, is to switch from high–phosphate detergents to soaps. If you live in a soft water area you can switch directly to laundry soaps such as Ivory Snow and Lux Flakes. If your water is hard and you are having a problem with soap scum, add a few tablespoons of washing soda (Arm & Hammer is a common brand). But a word of caution: if you have been washing with detergents, your clothes may be coated with detergent residues that will turn yellow when you first use soap and soda. To avoid this, wash once with hot water and soda (4 tablespoons) to strip off the residue.

Low- and non-phosphate detergents. The next best alternative to soap and soda is to use a low–phosphate or non–phosphate detergent or one of the high concentrate detergents that are sold by a number of direct sales firms. The important consideration is the quantity of phosphate per load of washing. On this basis, Amway's SA8 and Bestline B–7—of which you need to use one–eighth to one–fourth of a cup of detergent per washload—are less polluting than the standard brands that use one cup or more. Neither, however, has eliminated phosphates.

Look in the telephone book (white pages or yellow, under *Cleaning Compounds*) for a local distributor, or write to the company for the name of one.

The following companies produce cleaning products *some of which* are environmentally better than the standard brands. To the extent that they have led the way toward better products these companies are to be commended; however, judge their products on the same basis you would any competitor's—on pollution per washload and packaging. Ask them for information that will enable you to do this.

Amway Corporation
Ada, Michigan 49301

Bestline Products
Box 6416
San Jose, California
95150

Shaklee Products
Hayward, California 94544

Non–phosphate detergents are on the way. Shaklee Products of Hayward, California, has been marketing a line of organic cleaning products for some time. Their laundry product, Basic–L, is concentrated and has been promoted as containing no phosphates. Sears, Roebuck, & Company has announced that it will be marketing a newly formulated, non–phosphate detergent in September 1970 manufactured by DeSoto Corporation. And North American Chemical Corporation of Patterson, New Jersey, manufacturer of private label detergents for Finast, Shop–Rite, Waldbaum's, and other supermarket chains has also announced a new phosphate–free detergent. Even the big boys are getting into the act. Lever Brothers announced that a phosphate–free, NTA–built version of Cold Water All liquid laundry detergent would be available in retail stores in late July 1970. Procter & Gamble has indicated that it will use NTA, a non–phosphate builder, to cut phosphate use by 300 million pounds annually. They have been using NTA with polyphosphates in Gain and Cheer for some time.

Arm and Hammer points out that you can replace one

third of your detergents with their washing soda and get good results.

Two-stage washing. Another way to cut your use of phosphates is to wash twice, first with a small quantity of synthetic detergent, then with regular soap. This cleans as well or better than washing with synthetic detergent alone and cuts phosphate use to one–third, although it does use more water.

Presoaking with almost anything will improve washing performance.

Enzyme presoaks and detergents. The high–phosphate enzyme presoaks are not worth environmental costs. Don't use them.

The Reuss Committee makes the following recommendation:

> The enzyme presoaks are misnamed. They contain two–thirds or more phosphate. In reality, they are phosphate presoaks. Designed to be followed by another wash with a high-phosphate detergent, they double the phosphate pollution from each load of laundry. They ought to be banished from the market. They were marketed only within the past 2 or 3 years and therefore cannot be said to be "essential" for maintaining the American standard of sanitation. The cost in destruction of America's lakes and waters that these products do far exceeds their trivial contribution to the advancement of cleanliness.

The enzyme presoaks and enzyme–active detergents are supposed to operate on the principle that an extract of enzymes will act to break down the natural compounds in food and grass stains without being able to act on the unnatural, synthetic fibers that are used to make our clothing. Most natural fibers, such as cotton and wool, have been so modified chemically that the enzymes don't recognize them as natural. Although this sounds great in principle, performance does not measure up to the claims.

In addition, there have been reports of allergic reactions to the enzyme products. The enzyme dust presents a known hazard to the lungs of workers in manufacturing plants that make enzyme detergents.

Arsenic and boron. Arsenic has been identified as a potential detergent hazard by a Kansas engineer who discovered arsenic levels of 1 to 73 parts per million (ppm) in some detergents and presoaks he tested. Presumably, arsenic is introduced as arsenate, which is chemically similar to phosphates and contaminates them. Arsenic is known to cause skin reactions (contact dermatitis) and, at 50 ppm, to inhibit the healing of wounds. The U.S. Public Health Service recommends a maximum concentration in drinking water of 10 parts per billion (ppb), not far above the 2 to 8 ppb found in a Kansas River.

Although boron in minute concentrations is essential to the growth of green plants, at even relatively low concentrations it becomes toxic to plants. Boron is found in several commonly used cleaning products as borate.

The ways that we design our detergents, our washing machines, and our fabrics are all interrelated. Switching away from high–phosphate products may necessitate a few changes in the way clothes washers are "programmed." However, the allegation that banning phosphates will make automatic dishwashers "useless" and that American standards of cleanliness and sanitation will have to be sacrificed can and will be refuted in your own home.

How hard is your water?

Phosphates in detergents serve a number of purposes, but by far the most important is to soften the water. This is necessary because when the calcium and magnesium ions in hard water mix with the soap and surfactant molecules, bathtub ring and scum are formed.

A few products are formulated differently for different water conditions. All should be. Those that are include Finish and Electrasol automatic dishwashing detergents. Areas with softer water require far less phosphate than those with hard water. Most manufacturers ignore this fact, instead adding enough softener to meet the needs of a broad market. Thus, your product may contain much more phosphate than you need.

The degrees of water hardness in major U.S. cities are listed in Table 19. The table may give you a clue as to whether you are in a hard or soft formulation region.

Other factors that influence how much softener you need include the size of the washload, how dirty it is, and how much water you must soften. For instance, Swedish machines use a much higher ratio of clothes to wash liquor, and consequently use less water and less softener than American models.

Detergent labeling is unsatisfactory

"Bleach, borax and brighteners" really isn't terribly informative, and the few packages that do list ingredients are sometimes misleading. For instance, Cold Power offers the following "analysis":

>   *Active ingredients:*
>   Sodium Tridecyl Benzene Sulfonate, 10.000
>   percent.
>   4'5–Dibromosalicylanilide, .025 percent.
>   3,4'5–Tribromosalicylanilide, .025 percent.
>   Inert ingredients,* 89.950 percent.
>   * Functional cleaning agents up to 85 percent.

Included in the "inert ingredients" is *34% sodium tripolyphosphate*.

One side of the Beads O'Bleach box proclaims: "Safe: contains no chlorine"—while another side says: "Caution: keep out of reach of children. Do not take internally. If swallowed call a physician."

TABLE 19. POPULATIONS AND HARDNESS OF THEIR FINISHED WATER SUPPLIES

City	Soft water (0–60 ppm)	Moderately hard water (61–120 ppm)	Hard water (121–180 ppm)	Very hard water (over 180 ppm)	Not stated
Albuquerque, N. M.	8,048	168,999			12,071
Atlanta, Ga.	600,000				
Baltimore, Md.	1,387,000				
Birmingham, Ala.		396,900			
Boston, Mass.	2,000,000				
Buffalo, N. Y.					
Charlotte, N. C.	212,946				
Chicago, Ill.			592,982		
Cincinnati, Ohio		593,964	4,423,000		
Cleveland, Ohio			750,000		
Columbus, Ohio		744,000	1,675,000		
Dallas, Tex.		334,800			
Denver, Colo.	285,200				10,650
Detroit, Mich.		3,078,200			174,150
Hartford, Conn.	344,350	85,050			130,900
Honolulu, Hawaii	145,800	554,400			
Houston, Tex.	84,700				
Indianapolis, Ind.		750,000		500,000	
Kansas City, Mo.					
Los Angeles, Cal.		1,474,800		491,600	491,600
Louisville, Ky.		550,000			
Madison, Wisc.					
Memphis, Tenn.	600,000			135,000	
Miami, Fla.	330,000	220,000			
Milwaukee, Wisc.			867,084		
Minneapolis, Minn.	296,820	285,680			
Newark, N. J.					
New Orleans, La.	750,000	627,525			

City					
New York City, N.Y.	8,099,500			250,500	
Omaha, Neb.					
Philadelphia, Pa.		1,001,256	327,000		
Pittsburgh, Pa.		1,210,000	1,001,256		
Portland, Ore.	542,000				
Richmond, Va.	303,000				
St. Louis, Mo.		760,000			
Salt Lake City, Utah			146,880	103,360	21,760
San Antonio, Tex.				603,000	
San Diego, Cal.			24,000	342,000	234,000
San Francisco, Cal.	1,312,000	288,000			
Seattle, Wash.	734,739				
Tucson, Ariz.		77,279		154,557	
Washington, D. C.		1,100,000			
Wichita, Kan.		255,000			

Source: This table is abridged from a table (POPULATIONS AND HARDNESS OF THEIR FINISHED WATER SUPPLIES IN THE 100 LARGEST U.S. CITIES) in the Reuss Committee Report: "Phosphates in Detergents and the Eutrophication of America's Waters," April 14, 1970.

Note: Water softness or hardness is commonly measured in grains per gallon, 10 grains per gallon corresponds to 170 p.p.m.

Table 20 offers a list of typical ingredients of the sort that should be listed on the box of every laundry product.

TABLE 20. TYPICAL HEAVY DUTY DETERGENT FORMULATION

Sodium dodecylbenzene sulfonate—*surfactant*	18%
Sodium xylene sulfonate—*dedusting agent*	3%
Diethanolamide of coconut fatty acids—*foam booster*	3%
Sodium tripolyphosphate—*improves cleaning power*	50%
Sodium silicate—*anticorrosion agent*	6%
Carboxymethyl cellulose—*soil redeposition preventive*	.5%
Optical brightener—*fluorescent whitener*	.3%
Benzotriazole—*antitarnishing agents*	.1%
Water and other inorganic salts—*fillers*	19.1%

The Reuss Committee Report calls for reform in labeling practices. If the reforms it suggests can be implemented, consumers may finally be able to make rational choices in the supermarket. Although phosphates will someday be banned, there may be an interim period during which the following list (Table 21) of phosphate additives may help you make valid comparisons between brands.

TABLE 21. COMMON PHOSPHATE ADDITIVES

Abbreviation	Name	Factor
STPP	Pentasodium tripolyphosphate	3.95
TSPP	Tetrasodium pyrophosphate	4.29
TKPP	Tetrapotassium pyrophosphate	5.16
TSP	Trisodium orthophosphate	5.29
C1TSP	Chlorinated trisodium orthophosphate hydrate	12.30
Octadecene	Phosphonated octadecene	10.75

The additives contain different percentages of phosphorus. Thus, comparing detergents on the basis of percentage of phosphorus is more valid than comparison on the basis of percentage of additive. (In a full-page newspaper ad about detergents and phosphates, Procter & Gamble correctly pointed out that the phosphorus content of detergents is only a fraction of the phosphate additive percentage, implying, perhaps, that the smaller number means less pollution. This is not so.) To find the percentage of the additive, multiply the percentage of phosphorus by the factor given in the table. Thus, a detergent with 39.5% STPP contains 10% P, while one with 39.5% C1TSP contains only 3.2% P.

What are the phosphate levels?

Two lists of phosphate levels in detergents have been widely publicized. Agreement between them is far from complete. The master table (Table 22) that follows includes these lists, data supplied to the Reuss Committee by the manufacturers, and some tests done for the Federal Water Pollution Control Administration.

Many products could not be included in this list, and it must be remembered that the formulations for some of those that are included will change. If you cannot find the information you want in this table or on the detergent box, ask the store manager for the information or write the manufacturer. His address is printed somewhere on the box.

The detergent–caused eutrophication of inland lakes and rivers and, before it, the foam that was created by non–biodegradable detergents, have been two of the classic consumer–related environmental problems of the last decade. The irony of both problems is that Americans, while promoting cleanliness and sanitation to the point of fetishism, have so befouled the inland waters of the nation with detergent byproducts and other wastes that they no longer can support fish life. It has taken foaming tap water and the death of Lake Erie to move "Mr. Clean" —the soap and detergent industry—to take measures to abate this pollution. In neither case would the industry have moved as quickly without the vigorous protests of concerned consumers working with responsive legislators. But keep your eyes and ears open, for the concluding chapter in the detergent saga will probably never be written.

TABLE 22. PERCENTAGE OF PHOSPHORUS IN HOUSEHOLD SOAPS AND DETERGENTS

Product and Manufacturer	%P_1[1]	%P'_1[2]	Additive	%STPP[3]	%P[4]	%P[5]
I. AUTOMATIC DISHWASHING DETERGENTS						
Automatic Dishwasher All (Lever)	45		STPP ClTSP	54.0	13.7	11.2 1.6
Amway Automatic Dishwasher Compound (Amway)	34					
Calgonite (Calgon)	42		STPP TSP	49.4	12.5	12.4
Cascade (Procter & Gamble)	36.5		STPP ClTSP	54.5	13.8	11.3 1.8
Electrasol (Economics Lab.)						
Soft Water formula						5.54
Hard water formula				34.8 (?)		8.92
Finish (Economics Lab.)						
Soft water formula						4.53
Medium hard water formula						7.26
Hard water formula					11.1	10.89
Sears Automatic Dishwashing Detergent (DeSoto)		43 (?)				12.0
Swish (Curley Corp.)	29					

Sources: (1) Analyses performed by Limnetics Inc. of Milwaukee and first published in the *N. Y. Times*, December 15, 1969. (Percent phosphate, P_1)
(2) Analyses performed by Pollution Probe at the University of Toronto. (Percent phosphate, P'_1)
(3) Analyses performed for the Federal Water Quality Administration and published in the *N. Y. Times*, May 3, 1970. (Percent STPP)
(4) Federal Water Pollution Control Administration figures available in the *Hearings* (December 15 & 16, 1969) and *Report* (April 14, 1970) on "Phosphates in Detergents and the Eutrophication of America's Waters" Subcommittee on Conservation and Natural Resources of the Committee on Government Operations, (Percent phosphorus, P)
(5) Figures supplied by the manufacturers to the Subcommittee. (Percent phosphorus, P)

II. PRE-SOAK LAUNDRY PRODUCTS

Product						
Amway Tri-Zyme (Amway)	43.7	52.5			17.4	17.5
Axion (Colgate–Palmolive)	40.4				18.7	16.0
Biz (Procter & Gamble)			STPP			15.3
Brion (Purex)						
Sears Enzyme Presoak (DeSoto)						

III. LAUNDRY DETERGENTS AND SOAPS

Product						
Dash (Procter & Gamble)			STPP	63.2	14.7	14.7
Farm Service Laundry Detergent (DeSoto)				73.9		
Salvo (Procter & Gamble)	35.3		STPP	56.6	13.2	14.8
Tide XK (Procter & Gamble)	30.6	43.5	STPP	49.8	11.6	15.0
Blue Sail } (Great Atlantic &			STPP			12.4
White Sail } Pacific Tea Co.)			STPP			12.6
American Family Detergent (Procter & Gamble)			STPP			12.6
Cold Water All (Powder) (Lever)	9.8 (liquid?)		STPP	45.4	11.0	12.4
Sears Enzyme Laundry Detergent (DeSoto)			STPP			12.4
Sears Laundry Detergent (DeSoto)						11.4
Drive (Lever)	25.3	41.5	STPP	47.4	12.0	11.4
Oxydol (Procter & Gamble)	30.7	44.5	STPP	46.6	11.9	11.1
Ajax Laundry (Colgate–Palmolive)	28.2			44.6	11.3	11.8
Bold (Procter & Gamble)	30.2	32.5	STPP	45.4	11.3	11.5
Gain (Procter & Gamble)	24.4		STPP	39.5	10.0	10.5
Whirlpool Laundry Det. (DeSoto)						10.3
Dreft (Procter & Gamble)	24.5	34	STPP	41.9		10.1
Surf (Lever)		32.5	STPP	48.2	10.2	10.0
Rinso (Lever)			STPP			10.0
Punch (Colgate–Palmolive)	25.8			44.2	9.9	
Duz Detergent (Procter & Gamble)	23.1	35	STPP	38.3	9.7	9.8

Product and Manufacturer	%P_1[1]	%P_1[2]	Additive	%STPP[3]	%P[4]	%P[5]
Peri (Sep-Ko Chemicals)	22.3	47	STPP	37.5	9.5	9.8
Bonus (Procter & Gamble)			STPP			9.7
Silver Dust (Lever)			STPP			9.6
Concentrated All (Lever)		39				9.6
Cheer (Procter & Gamble)	22.0	44.5	STPP	36.3	9.2	9.7
Breeze (Lever)	22.2	32	STPP	37.2	8.6	
Bio-Ad (Colgate–Palmolive)	35.5	49			8.3	
Fab (Colgate–Palmolive)	21.6	36.5		34.8	9.3	
ABC (Colgate–Palmolive)		37.5				
Sunlight (Lever)		37				
Amway SA8 (Amway)		36.5		49.3		
Arctic Power (Colgate–Palmolive)		36.5				
Omo (Lever)	19.9	35				
Cold Power (Colgate–Palmolive)		27		44.6	8.2	9.0
Brillo Detergent (Purex)		27				9.0
News Detergent (Purex)		26				
Amaze (Lever)						
Bestline B–7 (Bestline Products)				38		
Explore (Witco Chemical)						
Maleo Laundry Detergent (Maleo Products)		25				
Sulframin HD Beads (enzyme detergent) (Witco Chemical)						8.8
Hudso (DeSoto)						7.6
Service Soft (DeSoto)						7.6
Pathmark Cold Water Detergent (Theobald)			STPP			7.6
Shop Rite Cold Water Detergent (Theobald)			STPP			7.6
Food Giant (Coast Detergents)			STPP			7.5

Product				Active Ingredient		
Lucky (Coast Detergents)				STPP		7.5
Market Basket (Coast Detergents)				STPP		7.5
O-So-Kleen (Coast Detergents)				STPP		7.5
Shopping Bag (Coast Detergents)				STPP		7.5
Statler Bros. (Coast Detergents)				STPP		7.5
Vons (Coast Detergents)				STPP		7.5
Suflramin HD Beads						
Blue (Witco Chemical)				STPP		7.2
White (Witco Chemical)				STPP		7.2
Easy Bright (Theobald)				STPP		6.8
Fyme Tex (Theobald)				STPP		6.8
Grand (Theobald)				STPP		6.8
Jet Power (Theobald)				STPP		6.8
Key Food (Theobald)				STPP		6.8
Pathmark All Purpose D (Theobald)				STPP		6.8
Shop Rite All Purpose D (Theobald)				STPP		6.8
Our Own (Stanson Chemicals)				STPP		3.75
Stanzal (Stanson Chemicals)				STPP		3.75
Supa-Safe (Stanson Chemicals)				STPP		3.75
Instant Fels (Purex)	1.4	9	16.6			3.0
Trend (Purex)			7.1		1.8	1.5
Duz Soap (Procter & Gamble)						
Ivory Snow (Procter & Gamble)						
Ivory Flakes (Procter & Gamble)						
Lux Flakes (Lever)						
Maple Leaf Soap Flakes (Canada Packers)						

IV. MISCELLANEOUS PRODUCTS

Product				Active Ingredient		
Zero (Boyle-Midway)	5.0		19.8	TKPP		
Amway L.O.C. Suds (Amway)		7.5				
Cold Water All (Liquid) (Lever)					4.8	4.8
Diaper Pure (Boyle-Midway)					5.0	3.0

Product and Manufacturer	% P_1 [1]	% P_1 [2]	Additive	% STPP [3]	% P [4]	% P [5]
Beads O'Bleach (Purex)						8.0
Miracle White Safety Bleach (Theobald)						
Pathmark Safety Bleach (Theobald)			STPP			1.3
Sage Safety Bleach (Theobald)			STPP			7.6
Shop Rite Safety Bleach (Theobald)			STPP			5.1
Snowy Bleach (Harold Schafer Ltd.)			STPP			7.8
Dutch Bleach (Purex)		22.5		36.4		
Javex Bleach (Bristol Myers)		.....				
Blu-White (Purex)						1.5
Calgon water conditioner (Calgon)		75.5				
Amway Water Softener (Amway)		73.5				
Amway Dish Drops (Amway)						
Gentle Fels (Purex)						.....
Dove Liquid (Lever)						.....
Ivory Liquid (Procter & Gamble)					0.2	.....
Joy (Procter & Gamble)						.....
Lux Liquid (Lever)						.....
Swan Liquid (Lever)						.....
Trend Liquid (Purex)						.....
Cinch (Procter & Gamble)			TSP.12H$_2$O			0.18
Thrill (Procter & Gamble)			TKPP			2.3
Explore Liquid (Witco Chemical)		.....				
Bestline Liquid Concentrate (Bestline)		23				
Solvease (Russel Chemical)						6.32
Soak-eze (Calgon)						13.54
Sparkleen (Calgon)						14.28
Spray-Off (Calgon)						

Product					
Car Wash Detergent No. 28 (Procter & Gamble)					18.1
Follow Charlie Car Wash (Calgon)					14.27
Spic and Span (Procter & Gamble)	STPP	21		6.38	5.0
Mr. Clean (Procter & Gamble)	STPP				3.8
Top Job (Procter & Gamble)	TSP				2.4
Wisk (Lever)	TKPP	10.5		2.8	2.4
Janitor-in-a-Drum (Texize Chemicals)	TKPP	7.6	14.2		3.4
20 Mule Team Household Cleaner (U.S. Borax)	TKPP				1.2
Ajax Floor and Wall Cleaner (Colgate-Palmolive)	STPP				2.0
Fantastik Disinfectant Spray Cleaner (Texize Chemicals)	STPP			4.23	
Hood Pine Detergent Ammonia (Texize Chemicals)					0.3
Pine Cleaner (Texize Chemicals)					0.6
Spring Scent Cleaner (Texize Chemicals)					0.3
Sun Glow Pine Scent Cleaner (Texize Chemicals)					1.1
Pinesol (Cyanamid)		.....			1.2
Lestoil (Noxema)		.....			
Ajax Cleanser (Colgate-Palmolive)	C1TSP	6.5		0.66	1.3
Comet Cleanser (Procter & Gamble)	STPP			2.76	1.7
Dutch Cleanser (Purex)				1.27	1.5

9. FOOD FROM THE MARKET

176

9. Food from the Market

So many environmental issues come up in the supermarket that it is impossible to do justice to all of them in a few pages. Nevertheless, this chapter will attempt to cover most of the important issues in enough depth so that you can begin to devise a personal strategy for environmentally sounder living.

In 1966 it was estimated that the typical supermarket carried about 8,000 different food items. The figure today is certainly higher. In addition, there is a wide selection of paper products, laundry and cleaning aids, pest controls, and toiletry articles.

The market is a facade for the vast network of middle men who take the grain, fruit, vegetables, and meat from the farmer, the wood from the forester, and other raw materials from the primary producers and process them into finished goods. If you are environmentally concerned, you care about what happens before the finished product reaches the market, because the manufacture and processing of some of the available goods creates unacceptable pollution. Other products, especially some foods, are so adulterated by the time they reach the market that they actually constitute a hazard to health.

FOOD

When you enter the market to shop for food, you are probably looking for several qualities. You want something that will be nourishing, appetizing, and convenient to prepare. It should be fresh, and, of course, safe to eat. Is this what you get?

TABLE 23. RECOMMENDED DAILY DIETARY ALLOWANCES FOR AMERICANS

Family Members	Weight (Pounds)	Height (Feet-Inches)	Calories	Protein (gms.)	Calcium (gms.)	Iron (mg.)	Vitamin A (I.U.)	Thiamine (mg.)	Riboflavin (mg.)	Niacin (mg. Equiv.)	Ascorbic Acid (mg.)	Vitamin D (I.U.)
MEN												
18-35 years	154	5-9	2,900	70	0.8	10	5,000	1.2	1.7	19	70	
35-55 years	154	5-9	2,600	70	0.8	10	5,000	1.0	1.6	17	70	
55-75 years	154	5-9	2,200	70	0.8	10	5,000	0.9	1.3	15	70	
WOMEN												
18-35 years	128	5-4	2,100	58	0.8	15	5,000	0.8	1.3	14	70	
35-55 years	128	5-4	1,900	58	0.8	15	5,000	0.8	1.2	13	70	
55-75 years	128	5-4	1,600	58	0.8	10	5,000	0.8	1.2	13	70	
CHILDREN												
1-3 years	29	2-10	1,300	32	0.8	8	2,000	0.5	0.8	9	40	400
3-6 years	40	3-6	1,600	40	0.8	10	2,500	0.6	1.0	11	50	400
6-9 years	53	4-1	2,100	52	0.8	12	3,500	0.8	1.3	14	60	400
BOYS												
9-12 years	72	4-7	2,400	60	1.1	15	4,500	1.0	1.4	16	70	400
12-15 years	98	5-1	3,000	75	1.4	15	5,000	1.2	1.8	20	80	400
15-18 years	134	5-8	3,400	85	1.4	15	5,000	1.4	2.0	22	80	400
GIRLS												
9-12 years	72	4-7	2,200	55	1.1	15	4,500	0.9	1.3	15	80	400
12-15 years	103	5-2	2,500	62	1.3	15	5,000	1.0	1.5	17	80	400
15-18 years	117	5-4	2,300	58	1.3	15	5,000	0.9	1.3	15	70	400

Source: The New York Times Encyclopedic Almanac, 1970

Good nutrition isn't a fad

The proper diet provides calories to meet the energy needs of the body, proteins to serve as building material, and vitamins and minerals. Energy is provided primarily by carbohydrates and fat. The balanced meal contains enough of each of the important food groups—milk products, meat, vegetables and fruits, breads and cereals—to meet all of the nutritional requirements with room to spare. (Consult *"Foods for Fitness, A Daily Food Guide,"* U.S. Department of Agriculture leaflet Number 424, 5¢ from the Government Printing Office, Washington, D.C. 20402.)

Table 23 presents the recommended daily dietary allowances, and table 24 summarizes the nutritional values in common foods. It is quite possible for any intelligent shopper to meet these requirements using the standard foods at regular supermarkets without the aid of any vitamin supplements. In the United States there is a supply of 3200 calories per capita per day, and the diet, on the average, is rich in protein. Few countries are as fortunate.

The average numbers, however, conceal a lot of nutritional imbalances. Neither starvation nor obesity is uncommon in the U.S. There are many people who, either because of their particular metabolisms or because they are not careful in planning their diets, don't get the proper balance of nutrients in their food. Unfortunately, the growing tendency seems to be toward do–it–yourself, commercialized cures—diet foods and nutritional supplements. People now place their trust in promotions devised by nutritionally ignorant advertising agencies instead of consulting professional nutritionists and physicians and correcting the problem at its source—the food they eat.

TABLE 24. COMPOSITION OF FOODS: MINERALS AND VITAMINS

		MINERALS				VITAMINS				
Fruits and Vegetables	Food Energy (cal.)	Protein (gm.)	Fat (gm.)	Calcium (mg.)	Iron (mg.)	Vitamin A Value (I.U.)	Thiamine B_1 (mg.)	Riboflavin B_2 (mg.)	Niacin Value (mg.)	Ascorbic Acid (mg.)
Apple, raw, 1 med. 2½" diam	76	.4	.5	8	.4	120	.05	.04	.2	6
Apple juice, fresh/canned, 1 cup	124	.2	—	15	1.2	90	.05	.07	tr	2
Applesauce, canned, unsweetened, 1 cup	100	.5	.5	10	1.0	70	.05	.02	.1	3
Banana, raw 1 large, 8 x 1½"	119	1.6	.3	11	.8	570	.06	.06	1.0	13
Beans:										
Red kidney, canned/cooked, 1 cup	230	14.6	1.0	102	4.9	—	.12	.12	2.0	—
Baked—pork & molasses, 1 cup	325	15.1	7.8	146	5.5	90	.13	.09	1.2	7
Carrots, raw, 1 5½" x 1"	21	.6	.2	20	.4	6,000	.03	.03	.3	3
Coleslaw, 1 cup	102	1.6	7.3	47	.5	80	.06	.05	.3	50
Corn, 1 ear 5" long	84	2.7	.7	5	.6	390	.16	.10	1.4	8
Fruit cocktail, canned, 1 cup solids and liquids	124	7.0	10.0	3	.6	—	.08	.09	1.3	—
Grapefruit, raw, 1 cup sections	77	1.0	.4	43	.4	20	.07	.04	.4	78
Canned in syrup, 1 cup, solids and liquids	181	1.5	.5	32	.7	20	.07	.05	.5	74
Juice, fresh, 1 cup	87	1.2	.2	20	.7	20	.09	.05	.5	99
Honeydew melon, 1 wedge 2 x 7"	49	.8	.5	26	.6	60	.07	.04	.3	34
Mushrooms, canned, 1 cup	28	3.4	.5	17	2.0	—	.04	.60	4.8	—
Nuts:										
Almonds, shelled, 1 cup	848	26.4	76.8	361	6.2	—	.35	.95	6.5	tr
Peanuts, roasted, 1 cup med.	805	38.7	63.6	107	2.7	—	.42	.19	23.3	—
Oranges, 1 med. 3" diameter	70	1.4	.3	51	.6	290	.12	.04	.4	77
Orange juice, 1 cup	108	2.0	.3	47	.5	460	.19	.06	.6	122
Peaches, raw, 1 medium	46	.5	.1	8	.6	880	.02	.05	.9	8
Pineapple, raw, 1 cup diced	74	.6	.3	22	.4	180	.12	.04	.3	33

Source: The New York Times Encyclopedic Almanac, 1970, adapted from U.S. Department of Agriculture, Handbook, No. 8

Potatoes, baked, 1 med. 2½" diameter	97	2.4	.1	13	.8	20	.11	.05	1.4	17
Peeled and boiled, 1 med.	105	2.5	.1	14	.9	20	.12	.04	1.3	17
French fried, 8 pieces	157	2.2	7.6	12	.8	20	.07	.04	1.3	11
Hash-browned, 1 cup	470	6.4	22.3	35	2.3	60	.15	.11	3.3	14
Mashed, milk added, 1 cup	159	4.3	1.4	53	1.2	80	.16	.10	1.7	14
Prune juice, canned, 1 cup	170	1.0	—	60	4.3	—	.07	.19	1.0	2
Rice, brown, raw, 1 cup	784	15.6	3.5	81	4.2	—	.66	.10	9.6	—
Cooked, 1 cup	204	4.2	.2	14	.5	—	.10	.02	1.9	—
White, cooked, 1 cup	201	4.2	.2	13	.5	—	.02	.01	.7	—
Spinach, raw 4 oz	22	2.6	.3	92	3.4	10,680	.13	.23	.7	67
Cooked, 1 cup	46	5.6	1.1	223	3.6	21,200	.14	.36	1.1	54
Watermelon, ½ slice	45	.8	.3	11	.3	950	.08	.08	.3	10
Meat, Fish and Eggs										
Bacon, crisp, 2 slices	97	4.0	8.8	4	.5	—	.08	.05	.8	—
Beef cuts, cooked:										
Chuck, 3 oz., no bone	265	22.0	19.0	9	2.6	—	.04	.17	3.5	—
Flank, 3 oz., no bone	270	21.0	20.0	9	2.6	—	.04	.17	3.5	—
Hamburger, 3 ounces	316	19.0	26.0	8	2.4	—	.07	.16	4.1	—
Porterhouse, 3 oz., no bone	293	20.0	20.0	9	2.6	—	.05	.15	4.0	—
Rib roast, 3 oz., no bone	266	20.0	20.0	9	2.6	—	.05	.15	3.6	—
Round, 3 oz., no bone	197	23.0	11.0	9	2.9	—	.06	.19	4.7	—
Sirloin, 3 oz., no bone	257	20.0	19.0	9	2.5	—		.16	4.1	—
Beef/vegetable stew, 1 cup	252	12.9	19.3	31	2.6	2,520	.12	.15	3.4	15
Chicken, raw, broiler, ½ bird (8 oz., no bone)	332	44.4	15.8	31	3.3	—	.18	.36	22.4	—
Roasters, 4 oz., no bone	227	22.9	14.3	16	1.7	—	.09	.18	9.1	—
Hens, stewing, 4 oz., no bone	342	20.4	28.3	16	1.7	—	.00	.18	9.1	—
Fryers, 1 breast, 8 oz., no bone	210	47.0	1.0	28	2.2	—	.13	.18	21.1	—
1 leg, 5 oz., no bone	159	29.1	3.8	21	2.6	—	.14	.34	8.0	—
Canned, boned, 3 oz.		25.3	6.8	12	1.5	—	.03	.14	5.4	—
Clams, raw, meat only, 4 oz.	92	14.5	1.6	109	7.9	120	.11	.20	1.8	—
Eggs, boiled, poached, 1	77	6.1	5.5	26	1.3	550	.05	.14	tr	—
Omelet, 1 egg	106	6.8	7.9	50	1.3	640	.05	.17	tr	—
Scrambled, 1 egg	106	6.8	7.9	50	1.3	640	.07	.17	tr	—
Flounder, 4 oz. (raw)	78	16.9	.6	69	.9	—	.08	.06	1.9	—
Frankfurters, 1	124	7.0	10.0	3	.6	—	.08	.09	1.3	—
Haddock, cooked, 1 fillet	158	19.0	5.5	18	.6	—	.04	.09	2.6	—
Halibut, broiled, 1 steak	228	33.0	9.8	18	1.0	—	.08	.09	13.9	—

	Food Energy (cal.)	Protein (grm.)	Fat (grm.)	Calcium (mg.)	Iron (mg.)	Vitamin A Value (I.U.)	Thiamine B₁ (mg.)	Riboflavin B₂ (mg.)	Niacin Value (mg.)	Ascorbic Acid (mg.)
Lamb:										
Rib chop, cooked, 3 oz., no bone	356	20.0	30.0	9	2.6	—	.12	.22	4.8	—
Shoulder roast, 3 oz., no bone	293	18.0	24.0	8	2.2	—	.10	.19	3.9	—
Leg roast, 3 oz., no bone	230	20.0	16.0	9	2.6	—	.12	.21	4.4	—
Liver, beef, 2 oz., cooked	118	13.4	4.4	5	4.4	30,330	.15	2.25	8.4	18
calf, 3 oz, raw	120	16.2	4.2	5	9.0	19,130	.18	2.65	13.7	30
chicken, 3 oz., raw	120	18.8	3.4	14	6.3	27,370	.17	2.10	10.0	17
Lobster, canned, 3 oz.	78	15.6	1.1	55	.7	—	.03	.06	1.9	—
Luncheon meat; boiled ham, 2 oz.	172	12.9	12.9	5	1.5	—	.57	.15	2.9	—
canned, spiced, 2 oz.	164	8.4	13.8	5	1.2	—	.18	.12	1.6	—
Oysters, meat only, raw, 1 cup	200	23.5	5.0	226	13.4	770	.35	.48	2.8	—
Stew, 1 cup (6-7 oysters)	244	16.6	13.2	262	7.0	820	.21	.46	1.6	—
Pork cured:										
Ham, smoked, cooked, 3 oz., no bone	339	20.0	28.0	9	2.5	—	.46	.18	3.5	—
Salmon, broiled, baked, 1 steak	204	33.6	6.7	—	1.4	—	.12	.33	9.8	—
Shrimp, canned, 3 oz., drained	110	23.0	1.2	98	2.6	50	.01	.03	1.9	—
Swordfish, broiled, 1 steak	223	34.2	8.5	25	1.4	2,880	.06	.07	12.9	—
Tongue, beef, med. fat, raw, 4 oz.	235	18.6	17.0	10	3.2	—	.14	.33	5.7	—
Tuna fish, canned, 3 oz. drained	169	24.7	7.0	7	1.2	70	.04	.10	10.9	—
Turkey, med. fat, raw, 4 oz.	304	22.8	22.9	26	4.3	tr	.10	.16	9.1	—
Veal, cooked, cutlet, 3 oz., no bone	184	24.0	9.0	10	3.0	—	.07	.24	5.2	—
Shoulder roast, 3 oz., no bone	193	24.0	10.0	10	3.1	—	.11	.27	6.7	—
Stew meat, 3 oz., no bone	252	21.0	18.0	9	2.6	—	.04	.20	3.9	—
Bread, Cereals, and Baked Goods										
Breads:										
Cracked wheat, unenriched, 1 sl.	60	2.0	.5	19	2.2	—	.03	.02	.3	—

Food										
Italian, unenriched, 1 lb.	95	39.5	3.6	59	3.2	tr	.23	.30	4.5	—
Raisin, unenriched, 1 slice	65	1.6	.7	18	.3	—	.02	.02	.2	—
Rye, American, 1 slice	57	2.1	.3	17	.4	—	.04	.02	.4	—
White, enriched, 4% nonfat milk solids, 1 slice	63	2.0	2.7	18	.1	—	.01	.02	.2	—
Toasted, 1 slice	63	2.0	.7	18	.1	—	.01	.02	.2	—
Whole wheat, 1 slice	55	2.1	.6	22	.5	—	.07	.03	.7	—
Cakes:										
Cupcake, 2¾″ diam.	131	2.6	3.3	62	.2	50	.01	.03	.1	—
Pound, 1 slice	130	2.1	7.0	16	.5	100	.04	.05	.3	—
Sponge, 2″ sector	117	3.2	2.0	11	.6	210	.02	.06	.1	—
Corn flakes, 1 cup	96	2.0	.1	3	.3	—	.01	.02	.1	—
Corn flour, 1 cup sifted	406	8.6	2.9	7	2.0	370	.22	.06	1.6	—
Doughnuts, cake type, 1	136	2.1	6.7	23	.2	40	.05	.04	.4	—
Oatmeal or rolled oats, 1 cup dry	312	11.4	5.9	42	3.6	—	.48	.11	.8	—
Cooked, 1 cup	148	5.4	2.8	21	1.7	—	.22	.05	.4	—
Pancakes:										
Wheat, 1 cake, 4″ diam.	59	1.8	2.5	43	.2	50	.02	.03	.1	—
Buckwheat, 1 cake, 4″ diam.	47	1.6	2.3	67	.3	30	.04	.04	.2	—
Puffed Rice, 1 cup	55	.8	.1	3	.3	—	.06	.01	.8	—
Rolls, 1 plain, unenriched (12/pound)	118	3.4	2.1	21	.4	—	.02	.04	.4	—
Shredded wheat, 1 large, biscuit	102	2.9	.7	13	.9	—	.06	.03	1.3	—
Spaghetti, dry, unenriched, 1 cup	354	12.0	1.3	21	1.3	—	.09	.06	1.9	—
Cooked, 1 cup	218	7.4	.9	13	.9	—	.03	.02	.7	—
Wheat germ, 1 cup stirred	246	17.1	6.8	57	5.5	—	1.39	.54	3.1	—
Milk and Milk Products										
Butter, 1 tbs.	100	.1	11.3	3	tr	460	tr	tr	tr	—
Cheese:										
Cheddar, 1 oz.	113	7.1	9.1	206	.3	400	.01	.12	tr	—
Cottage, from skim milk, 1 cup	215	43.9	1.1	216	.7	50	.04	.69	.2	—
Cream cheese, 1 oz.	106	2.6	10.5	19	.1	410	tr	.06	tr	—
Swiss, 1 oz.	105	7.8	7.9	262	tr	410	tr	.11	tr	—
Cream, light, 1 tbs.	30	.4	3.0	15	tr	120	tr	.02	tr	tr
Heavy, 1 tbs.	49	.3	5.2	12	tr	220	tr	.02	tr	tr

	Food Energy (cal.)	Protein (gm.)	Fat (gm.)	MINERALS Calcium (mg.)	Iron (mg.)	VITAMINS Vitamin A Value (I.U.)	Thiamine B_1 (mg.)	Riboflavin B_2 (mg.)	Niacin Value (mg.)	Ascorbic Acid (mg.)
Ice cream, plain 1/7 of quart	167	3.2	10.1	100	.1	420	.03	.15	.1	11
Margarine, 1 tbs.	101	.1	11.3	3	—	460	—	—	—	—
Milk, cow: whole, 1 cup	166	8.5	9.5	288	.2	390	.09	.42	.3	3
Fluid, nonfat (skim), 1 cup	87	8.6	.2	303	.2	10	.09	.44	.3	3
Canned, evaporated (unsweet), 1 cup	346	17.6	19.9	612	.4	1,010	.12	.91	.5	3
Malted beverage, 1 cup	281	3.4	.5	17	2.0	—	.04	.60	4.8	—
Yogurt, commercial, made with whole milk, 1 cup	170	11.0	8.0	560	.2	380	.10	.45	—	3
Others										
Candy:										
Butterscotch, 1 oz.	116	—	2.5	6	.5	—	—	tr	tr	tr
Caramels, 1 oz.	118	.8	3.3	36	.7	50	.01	.04	tr	—
Chocolate, milk, 1 oz.	143	2.0	9.5	61	.6	40	.03	.11	.2	—
Peanut Brittle, 1 oz.	125	.3	.1	2	.1	320	.02	.01	.4	—
Catsup, tomato, 1 tbs.	17	.3	.1	2	.1	320	.02	.01	.4	2
Chocolate syrup, 1 tbs.	42	.2	.2	3	.3	—	—	—	—	—
Cocoa, dry powder, 1 tbs.	21	.6	1.7	9	.8	tr	.01	.03	.2	—
Cola beverage, carbonated, 1 cup	107	—	—	—	—	—	—	—	—	2
Coffee, black, 1 cup	—	—	—	—	.1	—	tr	tr	tr	—
Jellies, 1 tbs.	50	—	—	2	—	tr	—	—	—	1
Macaroni & cheese, baked, 1 cup	464	17.3	24.2	420	1.1	990	.07	.35	.9	tr
Oils, salad/cooking, 1 tbs.	124	—	14.0	—	—	—	—	—	—	—
Peanut butter, 1 tbs.	92	4.2	7.8	12	.3	—	.02	.02	2.6	—
Pies: Apple, 4" sector	331	2.8	12.8	9	.5	220	.04	.02	.3	1
Blueberry, 4" sector	291	2.8	9.3	14	.7	160	.02	.04	.3	5
Cherry, 4" sector	340	3.2	13.2	14	.5	530	.04	.02	.3	2
Salad dressings: Commercial plain, (mayonnaise type), 1 tbs.	58	.2	5.5	1	.1	20	tr	tr	—	—
French, 1 tbs.	59	.1	5.3	—	—	—	—	—	—	—

Food										
Mayonnaise, 1 tbs.	92	.2	10.1	2	.1	30	tr	tr		
Salad oil, 1 tbs.	124		14.0							
Soups, canned:										
Bouillon, broth, consomme, 1 cup	9	2.0		2	1.0				.6	
Chicken, 1 cup	75	3.5	2.5	20	.5		.02	.05	1.5	
Clam chowder, 1 cup	86	4.6	2.3	36	3.6		.02	.12	.7	
Tomato, 1 cup	90	2.2	2.2	24	1.0	1,230	.05	.10	1.0	10[8]
Vegetable, 1 cup	82	4.2	1.8	32	.8			.08		
Sugars:										
1 teaspoon	16									
1 lump	27									
Yeast, dried brewer's, 1 tbs.	22	3.0	.1	8	1.5		.78	.44	2.9	

The assertion was made that it is possible to buy a balanced diet at the supermarket. This is challenged by some as not being true. These people contend that depleted soils rob produce of natural vitamins, that chemically fertilized crops are inferior, and that modern processing removes the nutritional value from food.

Defenders of present practices counter that poor soils cut down on yield, size, and appearance but not on nutritional value, that a chemical is a chemical whether naturally derived or artificially synthesized, and that vitamin enrichment can restore the nutritional values lost in processing. Without trying to decide which side is correct, several things can be observed.

■ There are enough other reasons why food should be organically grown that the depleted soil–deficient food argument is essentially academic.

■ Whether vitamin enrichment makes up for the missing nutritional value or not, it cannot be denied that today's selection of foods includes many that have very little nutritional value. This is especially true of the snack and diet foods that have flooded the market in the last few years.

■ Actually, it isn't so much what is absent from today's food that is important; it's the extra chemicals—the additives and the pesticide and packaging residues that are important.

Prepared food and food additives

Men have been adding salt and spices to food, smoking meat, and salting fish since prehistoric times. The large–scale of use of additives that is common today, however, is something quite new. There are reasons for it. Most people now live in cities. Because the distance between farm and market is greater, foods must last longer. As mechanization has taken over on the farm, the scale of operations has enlarged. The farmer no longer sells directly to the consumer or the grocer but to a distributor. The processing of food near where it is produced or at a central plant has opened up possibilities for cost–cutting that have been irresistible to the food industry. Old-fashioned methods cannot compete, with today's large–volume, mechanized, assembly–line techniques. Food manufacturing has become big business, backed up by the powerful advertising techniques possible with mass marketing and mass media.

Today's food industry has been made possible by additives. They prevent the aging of food—preservatives, anti–oxidants, stabilizers, sequestrants, and antistaling agents. These make the food–making machines happy (dough conditioners, anti–foaming agents). They allow industry to take shortcuts that save time and money (bleaching agents for flour). They restore properties that get lost in the elaborate processing (flavorings, colorings, vitamins). Additives have even been devised to make possible the use of other additives (emulsifiers for artificial flavorings). And additives permit the food technicians to otherwise modify the texture and taste, even to the point of creating wholly synthetic foods (thickeners, artificial flavors and sweeteners, flavor enhancers, artificial coloring, acidulants, alkalies, and buffers). There are many more.

Regulation of food additives is in the hands of the Food and Drug Administration (FDA). But until the Food Additives Amendment was enacted in 1958, the FDA could not act against a possibly harmful additive until foods containing it were in interstate commerce, and even then the burden of proof was entirely on the FDA. The 1958 amendment sought to turn things around somewhat. Now the FDA examines whether the additive is safe at the indicated levels of use and whether it performs its intended function, and then sets specific tolerance levels for different uses. However, when the amendment was put into effect, exception was granted for over five hundred additives in common use. These were placed on a "generally recognized as safe," or GRAS, list.

Sodium cyclamate, the artificial sweetener that was banned in October 1969 (effective in 1970), was on the GRAS list. Cyclamates were banned because they were found to cause cancer in the bladders of mice; the De-

laney clause of the Food Additives Amendment requires
a ban in this situation.

The cyclamate controversy illustrates the inadequacy of
the present system. The additive manufacturers don't like
the Delaney clause because it requires that anything that
causes cancer in animals be banned, even though it might
be safe in man. At the same time, new awareness of the
possible mutagenic (gene-altering) and teratogenic
(fetus-deforming) effects of additives suggest to others
that the Delaney clause, or some modification of it, should
be broadened to cover mutations, deformities, or any
other biological injury.

There is sure to be a continuing debate on this matter.
A review of the GRAS list is now underway. It is certain
that new evidence will continue to reveal new risks in
foods. Even natural foods contain biologically harmful
chemicals. In fact, many of the additives that are in common use, the harmful ones included, are of natural origin.
The risks will never be eliminated, but they can and
should be minimized.

Uninvited additives

The fact that mothers' milk commonly contains levels
of DDT four times higher than that found in cows' milk,
high enough to ban it from interstate shipment, has awak-
ened many people to the presence of uninvited additives
in our food. A report published in *FDA Papers* in June
1967 contained the results of a three-year study indicat-
ing that almost half of 49,000 randomly selected food
samples contained pesticide residues—29% of them more
than one pesticide. About 3% of the domestic samples
contained residues in excess of tolerances. The excesses
were less common in vegetables, fruits, and cereals and
more common in meat, fish, and dairy products.

FDA studies of fully prepared meals indicated that a
well-balanced diet in the U.S. contains:

chlorinated organic chemicals:	0.02	ppm
organic phosphate chemicals:	0.003	ppm

| chlorophenoxy chemicals: | 0.003 | ppm |
| carbamate chemicals: | 0.05 | ppm |

According to the FDA, these levels indicate that "a substantial margin still remains before residues in ready-to-eat foods even reach the currently acceptable levels." But what is "acceptable"?

The most pressing problem is with the persistent pesticides, mainly DDT and its companion chlorinated hydrocarbons. Because of their persistence and chemical properties, these chemicals tend to get more concentrated the higher up the food chain you go. The cow eats grass, she collects the DDT from the grass and concentrates it in her milk. Humans drink the milk and collect still-higher levels in their fat.

Similar concentration takes place in fish. Some Coho salmon from the Great Lakes have been taken off the market because of unacceptably high DDT levels. Mercury is another pollutant that has been found at high levels in fish in the Great Lakes. The discovery, in Spring 1970, of dangerous mercury contentrations in lake fish in Lake St. Clair and Lake Erie brought to a standing halt a $750,000-a-year commercial fishing industry there. Since then, mercury contamination of surface waters has been found in the Northeast and South. The source of most of it has largely been industrial waste discharges, notably by caustic-chlorine plants. Chlorine is used to "make safe" the effluent from sewage plants. Agriculture contributes a significant share of mercury to the environment as well. Seeds treated with mercurial fungicides have been known to reach man by way of the game birds he hunts.

The $450 million yearly market for animal health products, of which 20% is antibiotic feed additives and about 45% pharmaceuticals and biologicals, is another agricultural source of unintentional chemicals in human food. There is concern that the antibiotics or residues from them survive to contaminate our supply of meat and milk.

Farmers also use hormones to stimulate growth in animals raised for meat. The discovery ten years ago of high levels of growth hormones in chickens prompted the FDA to ban them in poultry production. Yet the practice of implanting pellets of the hormone diethylstilbestrol (DES) in steers' ears is common today. Very low levels of DES cause cancer in mice. Although the law states that no residue of the hormone is allowed in meat that reaches the consumer, recent evidence indicates that DES is detectable in about one of every 200 cattle slaughtered.

Other unintentional additives can migrate into foods from the packaging, for instance plasticizers from plastics, fillers in paper and cardboard, and glue and adhesives. Like food additives, packaging is regulated, but safety is less than assured. Like the growth in additives, the growth in modern food packaging is moving us in directions that create more potential hazards, not less. TV dinners and cook-in-a-pouch vegetables in which food is actually cooked in the packaging are two examples.

Back on the farm

Farming is big business. Its raw materials are land, water, seed, animals, and fertilizers. Its job is to turn out food; as much as possible. Modern agriculture has developed techniques that enable it to do this, including a large kit of chemical tools—fertilizers, defoliants, pesticides, and so on. Like any large industry, agriculture has also relied heavily on mechanization and on concentration of crops.

This concentration has ecological significance. A field growing only one crop is a monoculture, a very simple ecosystem. The simplicity breeds instability. A field of nothing but waving grain is an open invitation to any pests that happen to like waving grain. In a more complex system, the vulnerable plant would be protected by the presence of non-target plants that grow around it. The pest has a harder time finding its target and must travel more to infect neighboring plants. The farmer works for a trade-off—higher yields for a more vulnerable system.

The farmer also introduces varieties of plants and animals that are not suited by the climate. He then must modify the climate, by irrigation for example, and fight off the natural species that are better adapted to the location. Thus, cattlemen have sought to destroy the indigenous sage on the western plains with herbicides to make room for the grass that their cattle can eat. They have also killed the natural predators that attack their herds of cattle and flocks of sheep. But when the natural predators are gone, the smaller animals multiply unchecked and end up competing with the cattle for their grass. Agriculture tends to disrupt one ecosystem to replace it with another system that must be maintained by artificial means.

Thus chemical tools come in very handy. Herbicides kill the native plants. Pesticides prevent insect predators from destroying the crop. Enormous quantities of both are added to the environment because they are "needed" to produce more food. As farmers have become more sophisticated, they have "needed" more chemicals to improve efficiency. They use them to kill weeds in the field as an alternative to cultivating. In fact, they say that herbicides are preferable to mechanical weeding because the plants do not get bruised and this makes them less vulnerable to pests and disease. Herbicides also provide a convenient way to harvest such crops as cotton and potatoes more easily. The plants are defoliated first.

Growing crops draws a significant quantity of nutrients out of the soil. In a natural ecosystem the soil is replenished when the plant decays or when the animal that eats the plant fertilizes the soil with its manure. Harvesting breaks the cycle. To reclose it, the waste must eventually get back to the soil, or the nutrients must be replaced by some other means.

Oldtime farms managed this by returning the animals' manure to the fields. Industrial agriculture, however, finds that it is less expensive (in dollars) to concentrate the animals in feed lots and transport the food there. The manure never gets back to the land, because it is cheaper to use chemical fertilizer than to transport the manure. So the manure ends up in a river, which it pollutes, and the fertilizer comes from a polluting factory or phosphate mine.

Meanwhile the animals are confined in crowded, unhealthy feed lots. To prevent the outbreak of disease, their food is laced with antibiotics. This practice has the already-mentioned effect of contaminating the meat and another that is probably worse. The stomachs of the cattle are breeding grounds for antibiotic-resistant strains of bacteria, some of which infect man. Thus, routine use of antibiotics on animals is rendering those drugs ineffective in both animals *and* man.

In summary, the farmer, who should be a self-trained ecologist, has become instead an industrial manager who knows very little about the process he is managing. The food industry that, in many experts' opinion, has proven Thomas Malthus wrong, may prove him right.

In the potato chip factory

When the food leaves the farm, it enters the food processing plant, there to be turned into the product that you buy in the store. During the processing, a lot can happen to the food and to the environment.

What is in a potato chip? Well, to get 250 pounds of potato chips, a chipper must start with about 1000 pounds of potatoes. The potatoes are washed and peeled, sliced, rinsed, partially dried, and fried in fat or oil. A study of the industry published in 1960 indicated that in processing a typical 1000 pounds of potatoes, 1990 gallons of waste water or about 8 gallons per pound of chips was produced. Untreated, the waste included 25 pounds of BOD (biological oxygen demand) and 32 pounds of suspended solids. Waste is reduced in some plants by settling out some of the peelings, which have value as animal feed. About 40% of the chip is oil.

The potato chip has not been chosen as an example because it is an especially bad source of pollution. Rather it is illustrative of the sort of hidden costs that lie behind most of the purchases of food and other items that you make. Looking at the potato processing industry as a whole puts this in perspective. Per capita consumption of potatoes has held constant at about 110 pounds per year. In 1964 about 36 pounds per capita of this was processed into chips, frozen french fries, dehydrated diced potatoes, potato granules, flakes, flour, and starch. In every process a significant fraction of the potato is rejected: from 20 to 50 percent. Chipping is actually efficient in this respect as it uses abrasion peeling instead of steam or lye peeling. The latter—the most popular method in the U.S., also produces the most pollution per ton of potatoes processed, and the waste is highly alkaline, making it harder to handle.

An estimate has been made that the average daily tonnage of potatoes processed in this country generates an untreated waste load that is equivalent to that of a population of 5.5 million people. An FWPCA report which cities this statistic also points out that four of the nation's major fish kills in the period 1960–69 happened on the Snake River in Idaho as the result of inadequately treated potato waste. And then there is air pollution. So, what is in a potato chip?

TO THE MARKET

Having looked at the market in broad terms, you should be better prepared to revise your shopping strategy and, as necessary, your life style so that you can live more ecologically. There are two attitudes you can bring to this exercise. The first is a somewhat fearful, defensive one. The objective is to protect yourself and the environment around you from all of the hazards that man has created. The problem with this approach is that it is terribly easy to become overwhelmed.

The second approach is more optimistic. You place faith in the ability of your own body and in the capacity of the earth's ecosystems to absorb the insults that are thrown at them. You seek to understand how these systems work and how man's technologies work; and you try to minimize the insults to the things you value to the greatest extent that you can. The problem with the second approach is that it is terribly easy to lose concern.

Rather than vacillate between the two extremes, as

many people do, you should try to combine concern for survival with a faith that your contribution can make a difference.

Begin with a look at how you go about your shopping chores. Do you make weekly trips to the supermarket and buy in large quantities, or do you make a large number of smaller trips? Do you buy everything at the same store, or do you patronize specialty shops—the dairy, the bakery, the butcher shop? Remember that transportation costs, and that if you can't find what you want at one store, you can possibly find it at another.

You will have to tailor your shopping strategy to the opportunities in your area. There is no one "right" way to shop. It's a cinch, however, that if you stay in the supermarket rut, you will be less likely to find the ecologically sound products.

Ask your friends: Call up ecology groups to get their advice. Visit the small shops in your area and talk with the shopkeepers. Talk with the supermarket managers, too. In your explorations, you are almost certain to discover good things. It may be a dairy outlet that sells milk in returnable containers. It may be a butcher who doesn't package his meats in plastic trays and then wrap everything in plastic wrap. It may be a baker who makes his bread fresh each day from wholesome ingredients.

Check in the nearby countryside for on–the–farm shops that sell fresh produce in season. Find out whether there are any organic or natural food outlets nearby. Unless you can grow your own, these stores are the best source of food that is unadulterated by pesticides and food additives. The closest thing to a national clearing house for organic food information is Rodale Press of Emmaus, Pennsylvania 18049, which publishes the magazine *Organic Gardening & Farming*. They have put out a $1, 116–page booklet entitled the *Guide to Organic Foods Shopping and Organic Living*. Thirty–seven pages of this guide are devoted to a state–by–state listing of organic food sources.

There is a wide variety of stores—from expensive health

food stores to small family stores to the supermarket–sized operations that are beginning to come out of the co-operative market movement. In total there are now an estimated 2000 natural food stores in addition to the many roadside stands that are active on rural highways during the summer. Some areas of the country are better served than others. The movement is spreading, and your patronage and interest can help it work in your area.

HOME PREPARATION AND PRESERVING

Make it a policy to buy fresh foods, especially during the summer when they are available. Simply avoid buying frozen and canned food. Any decent cookbook will tell you how to prepare fresh foods that will taste more appetizing and be more wholesome. In this way you can also cut down on your contribution to packaging waste. You can prevent the pollution that occurs during the mechanical processing and the extended storage of commercial foods. If it is prepared in your own kitchen, *you* have control over the waste and can see to it that it doesn't pollute. Put the scraps in your compost pile.

If you feel ambitious or even just a little adventuresome, you should investigate home canning and freezing. You should time your effort to coincide with the harvest, when produce is plentiful and cheap. Then, with a stock of reusable jars, lids, and a stove, you can "put up" enough to supply you a good part of the way through the winter. Freezing is even easier. Several helpful publications are available from the Government Printing Office.

If you have produce from your own garden, canning and freezing are a good way to make use of any excess over and above what you immediately can eat. Home gardening (see Chapter 4) and home preserving are the best way to assure that your food is free from pesticide residues and additives.

Gardens and stores are not the only places that you can find food. With a knowledge of plants, you can find a banquet of berries, greens, roots, and other natural foods in any unsprayed field or forest. It isn't wise to go foraging without some knowledge of plants, because there are poisonous plants mixed in with the edible ones. *Stalking the Wild Asparagus* by Euell Gibbons is a good place to start acquiring such knowledge.

TABLE 25. LIVING OFF THE LAND

COOKED GREENS
Amaranth
Burdock
Cattail (buds and shoots)
Chickory
Dandelion
Day lily (buds and flowers)
Japanese knotweed
Milkweed (shoots, leaves and pods)
Wild mustard
Pigweed
Poke
Purslane
Wild asparagus

SALAD GREENS
Arrowhead
Calamus
Cattail shoots
Chickory
Dandelion
Day lily
Watercress
Wild mustard
Wild onion
Winter cress

BEVERAGES AND TEAS
Chickory root coffee
Dandelion root coffee
Basswood tea
Blackberry, raspberry, and strawberry leaf tea
Catnip tea
Cloverblossom and mint tea
Goldenrod tea
New Jersey tea
Sassafrass root tea
Sweet birch tea
Wintergreen or teaberry tea
Elder blow wine
Mulberry wine
Elderberry with scarlet sumac juice

WILD FRUITS
Wild apples and crabapples
Blackberries, dewberries
Huckleberries, blueberries
Wild cherries
Wild cranberries
Elderberries
Scarlet sumac
Wild grapes
Ground cherries
Juneberries, shadberries, or service berries
May apple or American Mandrake
Mulberries
The pawpaw
Persimmons
Raspberries and wineberries
Wild strawberries

SEEDS, NUTS, GRAINS
Acorns
Hickory nuts and walnuts
Sunflower seeds
Wild rice

ROOTS AND TUBERS
Arrowhead
Jerusalem artichoke
Great burdock
Calamus
Cattail
Day lily
Ground nut or Indian potato
Wild onion
Spring beauty or fairy spud

NATURAL FLOURS
Cattail pollen and dried root starch
Acorn meal
Amaranthus seed (ground)
Pigweed seed (ground)
Purslane seed (ground)
Sassafrass leaves (powder)
Sunflower seed meal

Source: *Stalking the Wild Asparagus* by Euell Gibbons

In addition to recipes for jams, jellies, and preserves made from the more obvious wild resources such as strawberries, blueberries, and apples, Gibbons describes a multitude of uses for such common but unrecognized "vegetables" as dandelions, cattails, and milkweed. Most of the plants he describes, for which he supplies a multitude of recipes, are listed in Table 25, grouped according to their uses.

COSTS

It is commonly believed that you have to pay a lot more to eat wholesome natural foods. This is usually not the case. If you live in a city and your only source of organic food is a natural food store that must import all of its food, that food will cost. If you try to buy fresh strawberries during the winter, they will, of course, be very expensive—if you can even find them. In season, however, most fresh produce is priced near or below the cost of processed equivalents. If you can deal directly with the grower, the costs are likely to be quite low; there are no middle men and no promotional or packaging expenses to jack up the cost.

Growing your own food or collecting it free in a field, at the seashore, or from a stream is least expensive.

Another way to reduce the cost of your food is to eat only enough meat to get the protein you need and no more. Understandably, it takes considerably more land and water to raise an animal than it does to grow an equivalent weight of vegetables. A mature steer eats 25 to 35 pounds of alfalfa each day and defecates 6 to 25 pounds of manure for each pound of weight gain. In the future, as pressures on agricultural production continue to grow, meat will become progressively more expensive than vegetables; and vegetable protein, supplemented as needed with the essential amino acids, will gradually displace meat protein. It is happening today—witness the ubiquitous soy protein and hydrolyzed vegetable protein on food labels.

The influence that industrial food manufacturing ex-

penses can have on the cost of highly processed food is
seen readily in a cost analysis of breakfast cereals that was
prepared by the National Commission on Food Marketing
in 1966. The farm value of the ingredients that go into a
41.6 cent box of cereal is only 4.3 cents. Of the remaining
farm–retail price spread, 4.9 cents is attributable to packaging, 8.3 cents to advertising, and 5.5 cents to profits
to the middle men who process and market the farmer's
grain!

Table 27 presents a summary of data about other grocery products from the same study.

TABLE 26. PRICE, MARGINS, AND COSTS OF A COMPOSITE ONE-POUND BOX OF BREAKFAST CEREAL, 1964

Prices Retail	Functions	Prices	Margins	Labor & Fringes	Packaging	Buildings & equipment	Advertising & promotion	Cartage & transportation	Other expenses	Profits (Pre-tax)
	Retailing	41.6	6.4	2.3	0.1	1.0	1.0		1.1	0.9
Into-store	Wholesaling and delivery	35.2	2.1	1.0		0.4		0.6	0.1	
	Intercity transportation		1.3					1.3		
F.o.b. plant	Processing	31.8	25.0	5.2	4.8	*2.3	7.3		†0.8	4.6
	Ingredient value	6.8	2.5							
	Farm to manufacturer costs							2.5		
Farm value	Total	4.3	37.3	8.5	4.9	3.7	8.3	1.9	4.5	5.5

*Other manufacturing expenses.   †General, administrative, and market research.

Source: "Cost Components of Farm-Retail Price Spreads for Foods," Technical Study No. 9, National Commission on Food Marketing, June 1966.

TABLE 27. PRICES AND SELECTED COST COMPONENTS OF GROCERY PRODUCTS, 1964

Product	Price (Retail)	Farm Value	Labor & Fringes	Packaging	Advertising	Profits (Pre-tax)
Butter, 1 pound	74.4¢	53.0	6.7	2.3	2.2	2.3
American process cheeze, 8 ounces	36.7¢	15.1	6.3	2.1	1.3	3.7
Evaporated milk, 14½ ounce can	14.9¢	6.4	1.3	3.0	0.9	0.8
Ice cream, half gallon	80.4¢	17.6	22.5	7.9	3.9	3.1
Fresh whole milk (retail), half gallon	47.7¢	21.7	10.2	3.0	1.6	2.5
Fresh whole milk (home delivered), half gallon	52.8¢	21.7	16.2	2.6	1.3	1.6
Beef (choice), 1 pound	70.8¢	42.4	12.1	1.4	2.0	2.0
Pork, 1 pound	52.3¢	26.6	14.5	1.2	1.8	1.6
Lamb (choice), 1 pound	70.0¢	39.5	14.3	1.7	2.1	2.0
Veal, 1 pound	78.1¢	40.6	16.7	1.8	2.6	2.3
Broilers (frying chicken), 1 pound ready-to-cook	36.3¢	19.7	7.1	1.5	1.2	1.2
Turkeys, 1 pound	40.6¢	26.0	5.3	2.5	1.2	1.6
Eggs, grade A, 1 dozen	51.5¢	29.1	6.6	3.1	1.7	2.2
A market basket of fresh vegetables and fruits	$100.00	33.07	25.71	6.43	2.50	2.86
Florida oranges, 90 pound box	$11.37	2.74	3.56	0.70	0.37	0.45
Washington delicious apples, 42 pound carton	$9.79	1.75	2.80	1.06	0.24	0.42
A market basket of processed vegetables and fruits	$100.00	20.84	23.77	13.77	6.47	3.70
Canned tomatoes, 303 can	16.0¢	2.6	4.5	4.0	0.7	0.5
Canned corn (cream style), 303 can	19.0¢	2.4	4.3	4.0	1.2	1.9
White bread, 1 pound loaf	20.70¢	2.33	8.17	1.41	1.05	1.14
Breakfast cereals, 1 pound	41.6¢	4.3	8.5	4.9	8.3	5.5

Source: "Cost Components of Farm-Retail Price Spreads for Foods," *Technical Study No. 9*, National Commission on Food Marketing, June 1966.

Another government study, performed in 1963 by the Marketing Economics Division of the U.S. Department of Agriculture, directly examined the "Comparative Costs to Consumers of Convenience Foods and Home–Prepared Foods." It was their finding that of 158 convenience foods that they looked at, 116 were more expensive than their home–prepared counterparts. Table 28 below summarizes some of the data they collected:

TABLE 28. COST PER SERVING: CONVENIENCE VERSUS HOME–PREPARED FOODS

Product	Serving (ounces)	Price (dollars)
French fried potatoes	2.0	
Home–prepared		0.0529
Frozen		0.0565
Mashed potatoes	3.5	
Home–prepared		0.0225
Dehydrated		0.0345
Boiled whole potatoes	4.0	
Home–prepared		0.0226
Canned		0.0456
Scalloped	4.3	
Home–prepared		0.0356
Dehydrated		0.0704
Corn on–the–cob	6.1	
Fresh		0.0820
Frozen		0.1030
Cut corn	2.9	
Fresh		0.0745
Frozen		0.0588
Canned		0.0618
Green beans	2.3	
Fresh		0.0426
Frozen		0.0567
Canned		0.0538
Green peas	2.8	
Fresh		0.1295
Frozen		0.0597
Canned		0.0503
Carrots	2.8	
Fresh		0.0305
Canned, sliced		0.0518
Canned, diced		0.0428
Orange juice	4.4	
Fresh, home squeezed		0.0757
Fresh, store squeezed		0.0714
Canned		0.0408
Frozen concentrate		0.0371
Lemon juice	1.1	
Fresh, home squeezed		0.0303
In plastic lemon		0.0623
Bottled		0.0210

Product	Serving (ounces)	Price (dollars)
Peaches	3.7	
Fresh		0.0580
Canned, drained solids		0.0926
Strawberries	3.5	
Fresh, drained solids		0.1210
Frozen, sliced, drained solids		0.1831
Frozen, whole, drained solids		0.2044
Canned, drained solids		0.2330
Rice, cooked	3.35	
Home–prepared, regular long grained		0.0117
Parboiled		0.0184
Precooked		0.0308
Spanish rice	4.46	
Home–prepared		0.0387
Canned		0.0597
Packaged combination		0.0677
Meat loaf dinner	11.0	
Home–prepared		0.2887
Frozen		0.6083
Beef dinner	11.0	
Home prepared		0.3192
Frozen		0.6061
Beef pie	8.0	
Home–prepared		0.1654
Frozen		0.2496
Fried chicken dinner	11.1	
Home–prepared		0.2395
Frozen		0.5863
Chicken fricassee	4.1	
Home–prepared		0.1510
Canned		0.1256
Salmon, cooked	1.9	
Frozen		0.1551
Canned		0.1512
Yeast rolls	1.3	
Home–prepared		0.0157
Complete mix		0.0213
Frozen		0.0216
Brown and serve		0.0401
Ready to serve		0.0496
Cherry pie	4.5	
Home–prepared		0.0674
Complete mix		0.0727
Frozen		0.1009
Ready to serve		0.1362
Waffles	3.3	
Home–prepared		0.0358
Incomplete mix (add milk & egg)		0.0373
Complete mix (add milk)		0.0326
Frozen		0.1106
Sugar cookies	0.5	
Home–prepared		0.0133
Complete mix		0.0173
Chilled in roll		0.0201
Ready to serve		0.0164

Product	Serving (ounces)	Price (dollars)
Baby food, peaches	4.75	
Home prepared from fresh peaches		0.0740
Commercially manufactured		0.1007
Baby food, peas	4.75	
Home prepared from fresh peas		0.2194
Commercially manufactured		0.0998
Baby food, beef liver	3.50	
Home–prepared, fresh liver		0.2032
Commercially manufactured		0.2468

Source: "Comparative Costs to Consumers of Convenience Foods and Home–Prepared Foods," *Marketing Research Report No. 609*, U. S. Department of Agriculture.

The study summarized its findings in terms of a calculated $100 grocery bill of which $12.55 was spent for convenience foods that could have been bought fresh or home–prepared for $12.82. The greater economy of most home–prepared foods was offset primarily by the low prices of a few convenience items, notably canned and frozen orange juices, canned and frozen peas, canned cherries, and cut corn, lima beans, and spinach.

TABLE 29. AN ANNOTATED $20 SHOPPING LIST

The first part of each section of this shopping list was compiled in a large supermarket with the intent of emphasizing the multitude of over-packaged and highly processed foods. The second part of each section contains a discussion of some of the alternatives.

SUPERMARKET BREAKFAST ITEMS	AMOUNT	COST
Carnation Instant Breakfast	7.44 oz. net	63¢
(six individually-wrapped packets in a cardboard box)		
Kellogg's Snack Pack	5 oz. net	47¢
(six individually-boxed servings of cereal overwrapped with plastic)		
General Mills Lucky Charms	9 oz. net	36¢
(sugar-frosted oat cereal with marshmallow bits)		
Pasteurized Homogenized Milk	two ½-gallons	$1.12
(two plastic-coated paper, half gallon containers)		
Nestea Iced Tea Mix	@ 1.7 oz. each	89¢
(11 individual foil-lined packets inside a plastic bag)		
ReaLemon reconstituted lemon juice	4½ fl. oz.	34¢
(in a plastic lemon with a "peel" that will never degrade)		
Carnation Coffee-Mate non-dairy creamer	6 oz.	37¢
(in a glass jar with paper label and metal lid)		

BREAKFAST ALTERNATIVES	AMOUNT	COST
The breakfast cereals can be purchased in larger boxes:		
Kellog's Raisin Bran	15 oz. net	38¢
General Mills' Wheaties	18 oz. net	44¢
(the large package of a relatively unprocessed cereal)		

The milk can be bought in returnable gallon jugs (a 25¢ deposit on the jugs)   95¢

Cream, suitable for coffee or whipping, can be bought in returnable
    glass bottles (a 5¢ deposit)   59¢
Real lemons can be bought at the Haymarket, Boston's open–air market,
    in July for 50¢ per dozen.
Other fresh fruit prices at the Haymarket:

Oranges 79¢/dozen	Peaches 69¢/dozen
Limes 25¢/5	Bartlett Pears 39¢/6
	Bing Cherries 75¢/2 lbs.

SUPERMARKET LUNCH AND SNACK

ITEMS	AMOUNT	COST
Wonder white, enriched bread	1 lb.	30¢
(What Frenchman would buy a 'wonder' bread?—R. Nader)		
Kraft–American cheese slices	12 oz.	58¢
(16 slices each individually-wrapped in plastic with a plastic over-wrapping)		
Nepco imitation chicken loaf lunch meat	8 oz.	65¢
(on a card with a plastic overwrap)		
Genoa Sliced Pepperoni	4 oz. net	65¢
(in a plastic and foil packet)		
Caterer's Kitchen Fruit Salad Gelatin	16 oz.	39¢
(in a discardable plastic dish)		
Campbell's Chicken and Rice Soup	10½ oz. net	16¢
(in a tin can)		
Stop and Shop Frozen Pizza with cheese	1 lb.	75¢
Burry's Corn Skis Snack	4½ oz. net	43¢
(in a cardboard can with metal ends)		
Nabisco Snack Mate American cheese spread	4¾ oz.	59¢
(pasteurized cheese spread in an aerosol can)		
Cool Whip non-dairy topping	4½ oz. net	27¢
(in a plastic dish)		
Fresca		$1.05
(eight 10 oz. bottles, non-returnable, in a cardboard pack)		

ALTERNATIVE LUNCH AND SNACK ITEMS

Truly fresh bread can be purchased at bakeries. If some of it should
turn stale, you won't have to buy bread crumbs.

Eggs can be bought in styrofoam or cardboard cartons. Choose the
cardboard cartons.

Kraft–American cheese slices   12 oz.   53¢
  (the same cheese without the individual wrapping, only the plastic
  overwrap)

The lunch meats can be bought at the meat counter of a grocery
store or at a butcher's shop without the atrocious packaging.

The fruit salad gelatin can be made from regular gelatin mixes without
much effort and without the plastic dish.

Home–made soups are a good way to take care of left–overs. Boil the
bones from the meats that you eat to get the stock.

SUPERMARKET DINNER ITEMS

	AMOUNT	COST
Swanson Loin of Pork TV Dinner	10 oz. net	67¢
Swanson Fried Chicken TV Dinner	11½ oz. net	49¢
(on a disposable aluminum tray, boxed)		
Lipton Beef Stroganoff with noodles and soy protein		74¢
(Makes two 11½ oz. servings. Ingredients are in three packets inside cardboard carton)		
Armour beef meat loaf with gravy	2 lbs.	$1.98
(boxed and frozen)		

Weaver fully-cooked, batter dipped chicken (boxed and frozen)	1¾ lbs.	$1.79
Caterer's Kitchen Fresh Chopped Onions	10 oz.	29¢
Caterer's Kitchen Macaroni and Cheese (in disposable plastic dishes)	12 oz.	34¢
Green Giant Broccoli and Noodles Casserole (boxed in a metal decorator tray that has a plastic cover)	12 oz.	39¢
Green Giant Sweet Peas in Butter Sauce	10 oz.	26¢
Green Giant Rice Pilaf with Mushrooms and Onions	12 oz.	37¢
(in plastic-coated cardboard boxes, vegetables are in plastic cooking pouches)		
Birdseye deluxe Whole Green Beans	9 oz.	33¢
Borden Whipped Potatoes (ten ½-cup servings, dehydrated in a box)		23¢
Minute Rice enriched and precooked (twelve ⅔-cup servings, in a cardboard box)	14 oz. net	44¢
Durkee Sour Cream Sauce Mix (makes ⅔ cup, in a foil-lined packet)	1½ oz. net	27¢
Betty Crocker Yellow Cake Mix (add eggs, in a waxed paper-lined box)	18½ oz.	36¢
Betty Crocker Sour Cream Chocolate Flavor Frosting Mix (boxed)	13 oz.	36¢
Beechnut Baby Foods (strained bananas, pears, etc.) (In small glass jars with metal lids)	4¾ oz.	9¢

One weekend, Vegetables were selling for the following prices in the supermarket. Of course they were all packaged in plastic.

Tomatoes 39¢/14 oz.	Corn on the cob 39¢/5
Lettuce 39¢/head	String Beans 29¢/lb.
Green Peppers 29¢/3	Peas in the pod 25¢/lb.
Oranges 69¢/8	Bing Cherries 59¢/lb.

ALTERNATIVE DINNER ITEMS

Haymarket (Boston's open–air market) prices for fresh vegetables (in July) on the same weekend:

Tomatoes 50¢/4 lbs.	Potatoes 69¢/10 lbs.
Celery 25¢/bunch	Eggplant 25¢/each
Lettuce 25¢/2 heads	Corn on the cob 35¢/dozen
Green Peppers 39¢/dozen	String Beans 35¢/3 lbs.
Onions 29¢/4 lbs.	Peas in the pod 25¢/3 lbs.
Cucumbers 25¢/6	Carrots 25¢/2 lbs.
Radishes 35¢/3 bunches	

Clearly it pays to find a good open air market. There is a similar saving possible if you can find a good butcher shop.

Regardless of the exact figures, it is clear that buying the so–called convenience foods does not save a significant amount of money. It is also clear that you can reduce your food bill by preparing certain foods in your own kitchen instead of buying the commercial equivalents.

It would be a mistake to dwell too much on cost, because you probably make your food purchases more on

the basis of what tastes good to you and what saves you
time and effort. To these two factors, plus cost, you are
asked to add the considerations of food manufacturing and
packaging and food safety. In many cases, the choice
boils down to "convenience" versus everything else. Be
willing to put "convenience" in its proper place.

PACKAGING

"The packaging industry has never viewed
disposability as a criterion of design. On the
contrary, the industry's aim has been to create
packages that would *not* crush, break, dissolve,
bend, fade, collapse, burn, etc."
—*The Role of Packaging in Solid Waste Management*

In today's supermarket, essentially every product is
packaged in one way or another. Even citrus fruit, which
has natural packaging, ends up enclosed in plastic bags.
Consumer and industrial packaging is big business.

Table 30 gives a breakdown of the per capita consumption of packaging materials in the period from 1958 to the
present and projects beyond this. In these gross statistics,
one can see clearly the growth in the amount of packaging
that each of us uses—especially in the use of plastics.

The 577-pound annual consumption figure translates
into a daily use of 1.6 pounds per capita. Because 90%
of this packaging ends up as refuse, it is clearly a significant contributor to the total quantity of waste that we
must deal with. You can see the extent of the contribution
of packaging to the municipal refuse load in Table 16 in
Chapter 7.

Packaging is expensive

In 1966, industry spent about $29 billion on packaging, $16.2 billion of which went for materials—51.7 million tons of it. The consumer packaging component of

TABLE 30. PER CAPITA CONSUMPTION OF PACKAGING MATERIALS BY KIND: 1958–1976

In pounds per capita

Type of Material	1958	1959	1962	1964	1965	1966	1970[a]	1973[a]	1976[a]
Paper and paperboard	189.3	207.2	216.4	229.4	241.2	255.5	283.6	307.0	332.1
Metals	72.0	73.8	73.3	68.8	69.5	72.6	73.1	74.3	75.7
Glass	67.8	71.9	71.7	76.8	80.7	83.6	92.2	97.8	107.0
Plastics	4.2	4.9	6.9	8.4	9.7	11.2	17.6	22.0	28.2
Wood	41.2	44.1	40.0	39.7	40.4	41.2	40.7	40.3	39.8
Textiles	3.3	3.3	2.9	2.6	2.4	2.6	2.0	1.6	1.3
Total	377.8	405.2	411.2	425.7	443.9	466.7	509.2	543.0	584.1
Miscellaneous	26.6	29.1	39.0	48.3	54.3	58.3	68.4	72.5	77.0
Grand Total	404.4	434.3	450.2	474.0	498.2	525.0	577.6	615.5	661.1

[a] denotes projection

Source: (U.S. Department of Health, Education and Welfare, *The Role of Packaging in Solid Waste Management 1966 to 1976*)

this was about $10 billion, and that translates into more than $50 per person. For a family of four, then, $200 of the money you spend each year goes for packaging. A 1967 survey by the trade magazine *Modern Packaging* indicated that an average of 18.6 cents of the gross sales dollar went for packaging costs. The percentage varied with the type of product and the type of container, as is indicated in the illustrative list of packaging–cost percentages they provided:

TABLE 31. PACKAGING–COST PERCENTAGES AT THE FACTORY.

Paint in an aerosol can	16%
Paint in a conventional metal can	5%
Toy in a film–overwrapped carton	14%
Toy in a blister pack	8%
Motor oil in a metal can	26%
Motor oil in a fiber can	10%
Small appliance in a corrugated carton	6%
TV set in a corrugated carton	1%
Beer in a tinplate can	43%
Beer in a one–way glass bottle	36%
Frozen food in a boil–in bag and carton	10%
Frozen fish in a carton	5%
Moist pet food in a metal can	17%
Dry pet food in a carton	9%
Cereal in a folding carton	15%
Corn meal in a paper bag	5%
Analgesic in a plastic bottle	10%
Antibiotic in a plastic bottle	1%
Baby food in a glass jar	36%
Baby juice in a metal can	33%

Source: *Modern Packaging,* May 1967

As you can see in Table 31, 43% of the money you spend for a beer goes directly into the trash can, 36% of what you spend for baby food, and so forth. This is horrendously wasteful, especially when there are readily available alternatives.

In general, any reusable container will be less expensive, as long as it is reused. Also, a large container will be proportionately less expensive because there is less packaging per product. In mathematical terms, the volume increases as the cube of the size while the amount of material in the packaging increases only as the square of the size. Whether this makes sense to you or not, it is easy to see the difference by comparing the cost per fluid ounce of Pepsi bought in different containers:

Container	Cost
12-ounce returnable bottles	0.90¢/fl. oz.
26-ounce no–deposit bottles	0.94¢/fl. oz.
10-ounce no–deposit bottles	1.22¢/fl. oz.
12-ounce cans	1.23¢/fl. oz.

The same effect can be seen very dramatically in breakfast cereals, where packaging costs push the one–serving –per–box cereal price higher than what a comparable weight of steak would cost.

It is interesting to note some of the factors that allow wide differences in packaging costs to coexist. Metal beverage cans, for example, have an advantage over the less–expensive glass bottles because they can be filled more rapidly in the bottling plant. They have already surpassed glass in beer sales and they are moving up in soft drink sales as well. The development of a new machine that can fill a glass–plastic composite bottle at even higher speeds may project such a container onto the market.

It is very clear that considerations other than cost determine what packaging is used. One of the key factors in the rise of packaging has been the advent of the self–service store. The package now has to sell the product. The medium has become the message. This is most flagrantly seen in the bubble–pack (large piece of cardboard, tiny trinket, all encased in plastic) that is so commonly used to sell novelty items. Packaging materials are chosen today because they help to get the buy–buy–buy message across.

Convenience also sells products and their packages. Throw–away bottles and cans, dinners that cook in their foil packages, boil–in–a–bag vegetables, and twist–off caps on beverage bottles all provide convenience in their use, if not in their disposal.

Composite packaging innovations have made packaging more versatile in meeting some of the marketing challenges mentioned above. Laminated plastic–paper–foil orange juice cans, plastic–coated paper milk cartons, cellulose windows in paper boxes, metal caps with plastic liners on glass bottles, and many others illustrate what has become a major trend in packaging.

Only recently have environmental considerations figured into the equations at all. This is obvious, when one considers where the trends are taking us.

■ Greater amounts of packaging mean that more paper, plastics, and metals must be manufactured.

■ More packaging means more solid waste.

■ The increase in the use of disposable containers increases the waste burden.

■ The move toward more composite materials makes any expansion of today's meager recycling efforts less likely tomorrow.

Table 32 summarizes some of the considerations you should take into account when you evaluate a product in the market.

What can you do about excess packaging?

Start by bringing your own shopping bag or basket to the store with you.

■ Politely decline to have your purchase bagged whenever it isn't necessary, and explain why. Convert the sales clerks.

■ Whenever a product is available in a returnable or reusable container, buy that form. Even today, milk and other beverages are usually sold somewhere in returnable bottles. Look for them.

■ Be sure you return all returnable bottles.

■ To make a point, return all *non*-returnable bottles and cans as well.

■ Leave any unnecessary overwrap at the store before you go home. Explain to the store manager why his toothpaste tubes shouldn't be boxed.

■ Judge a product, in part, by the container it comes in. Boycott products sold only in unacceptable containers. Don't buy cheese slices individually wrapped in plastic.

■ Don't buy products in aerosol cans.

TABLE 32. DESIRABILITY AND UNDESIRABILITY OF PACKAGING

Kind of Packaging	Item	Rating
No packaging or natural packaging	Citrus fruit	The best possible.
Returnable containers		
Glass	Soft drinks and beer	Good, as long as the containers are actually returned.
Plastic	Milk	
Reusable containers	Cookie tins	Good, as long as the containers are actually used.
	Potato chip cans	
	Cigar boxes	
	Steel drums	
Non-coated paper	Bags for candy	Eventually disintegrates
	Wrapping paper	Readily composts
		Litter is a problem.
Non-coated cardboard	Boxes	Has more fiber than paper
		This is the only area where significant recycling now takes place.
Glass	Jars	Eventually degrades to sand
	One–way bottles	Can be recycled.
All-the-same-metal cans	Regular cans	Can be recycled.
Steel	Beverage cans	As litter, steel will eventually rust.
Aluminum		Aluminum is forever.
Steel cans with aluminum tops	Pop-top cans	The steel can be recycled; the aluminum is lost.
Glass bottles with twist-off caps	Soft drinks	The metal ring around the top reduces the value of the cullet.

Kind of Packaging	Item	Rating
Wax paper	Box liners	If it's really wax, it will eventually deteriorate.
Standard "tin" cans	Canned fruits and vegetables	The tin (coating) and lead (solder) contaminants render these useless for recycling. (No detinning plants are active today.) As litter, they eventually rust.
Cellophane, plastics (NOT PVC, see below)	Windows in paper boxes / Plastic bags	Won't degrade. Resists composting, but will burn.
Plastic-coated paper	Paper milk cartons	The plastic coating prevents the paper from decomposing.
Plastic foam Styrofoam	Egg cartons / Packing	Adds bulk to plastic's non-degradability.
Polyvinylchloride plastics (PVC)	Clear plastic bottles / Stretch plastic wraps for meat and fruit	Non-degradable. When burned, generates hydrochloric acid gas which corrodes any metal around (e.g. the incinerator).
Polyvinylidene chloride	Saran	Non-degradable. The foil is not burnable.
Aluminum foil-plastic-paper laminates	Orange juice "cans" / Foil-lined boxes and bags	Lasts forever. Can't be recycled. Resists separation in segregation systems.
Aluminum foil	By the roll for home uses	

Collapsible metal tubes	Toothpaste	Not reusable, recyclable or combustible.
Aerosol cans	Toiletries Deodorants Hairsprays Spray paints Food products	Enormous amount of packaging per unit net weight. Not reusable, recyclable. A hazard (explosion), even when empty.

Also:
- Any aluminum product is expensive in terms of environmental costs. It takes about 10 kilowatt-hours of electricity just to make a pound of it.
- "Degradable" plastics have been heralded, but they have not come on the scene yet. It remains to be seen whether they really do break down into harmless products.
- Twine is preferable to rubber bands.
- Anything that is readily discardable is potential litter.

■ Don't buy TV dinners and pot pies that come with a metal cooking dish that is discarded.

■ Don't buy aluminum foil for home packaging of foods. Let yourself run out; you will be able to get along without it. Use permanent, reusable containers instead.

■ Don't buy plastic or paper bags. You probably have a sufficient supply without spending money for them.

■ Use a lunch box, rather than a paper bag.

■ Buy your ice cream in a cone instead of a discardable plastic dish.

> The Chinese fortune cookie is the ultimate—an edible package with inedible contents.

Right on, store manager!

The following letter was written by the manager of a Boston area supermarket to the chain's grocery division head after a shopper returned her unused or unusable extra packages and bottles to the checkout counter:

"I thought you would like to be apprised of this movement & perhaps you could do what you can to help control this trash problem & the resultant pollution problem. A lady just returned to me her non–returnable bottles, her overwrap on produce, her overboxed items like vanilla, alka seltzer, aspirin, etc. When you look at it from this angle & plus multiply it many times over you can see the ramifications if this continues to go about unabated."
—*Boston Area Ecology Action Newsletter* #2

DEFENDING AGAINST CHEMICALS

In theory, the consumer should be protected from unsafe food by the regulatory power of the Food and Drug

Administration. Unfortunately, FDA falls far short of meeting its responsibilities. The reader is referred to *The Chemical Feast* by James S. Turner, one of the reports prepared by Ralph Nader's Center for the Study of Responsive Law, for an account of FDA's failure to accomplish its assignment.

As the law is written, food standards define a set of mandatory ingredients which are present in any food that has a particular name. Thus, bread always contains flour, milk a certain percentage of fat, and so forth. Ingredients of this nature do not have to be listed on the food package. Optional ingredients, such as preservatives, thickeners, and artificial flavorings are supposed to be listed. In practice, however, many ingredients fail to appear. The FDA has created a third category—permissible ingredients, of which there are over 200—which can be added without listing. In other cases, they have merely ruled additives to be "required"; thus Coca Cola doesn't have to list caffeine as an additive in Coke.

The second hole in the defense against unsafe foods is the failure of the FDA to study with sufficient care the additives that it allows to be commonly used.

Thus, you, the consumer, are in the unhappy position of knowing that you take risks every time you eat, but not being able to find out enough to protect yourself adequately. To paint a picture this bleak is to overstate the situation slightly. As any inveterate label reader knows, it is possible to get at least an impression of how much of a product is real food and how much chemicals.

Sample Ingredient Lists from Labels

Ingredient listings from several labels are reprinted below for reference. Contrast

SWANSON DEEP DISH BEEF PIE
65¢ 16 oz.

Ingredients: Beef Broth, Cooked Beef, Enriched Wheat Flour, Water, Animal and Vegetable Shortening, Potatoes, Onions, Tomatoes,

Carrots, Peas, Vegetable Oil, Celery, Salt, Modified Food Starch, Dextrose, Monosodium Glutamate, Caramel Color, Yeast Extract and Hydrolyzed Milk Protein, Lactic Acid, Spice and Flavoring.

with

KRAFT WHIPPED TOPPING for desserts
49¢ Net Wt. 9.8 oz.

CONTAINS NO MILK OR MILK FAT. A Pasteurized Blend of Water, Hydrogenated Vegetable Oil, Sugar, Propylene Glycol Monostearate, Sodium Caseinate, Flavoring, Potassium Phosphate, Salt, Polysorbate 60, Monoglycerides, Sorbitan Monostearate, Lecithin, Cellulose Gum, Carob Bean Gum, Carrageenan, Artificial Coloring, Propellents: Nitrous Oxide, Chloropentafluoroethane, Carbon Dioxide.

CAINS KORN KURLS   39¢ Net Wt. 6 oz.

Ingredients: Processed corn meal, veg. oils, cheese flavor, salt, artificial color, artificial flavor, BHA & BHT added as preservative.

The whipped topping is worthy of special note. It is an example of an imitation food. The law requires that it be clearly labeled so that it will not be mistaken for what it isn't; in this case, whipped cream. You should have no trouble distinguishing other products of this type—non-dairy creamers, orange drinks and ades, and so forth.

Despite such labeling, a frightening number of Americans seem willing to fill their diets with such nutritionally unexciting "foods" as the following:

FRESCA

Contains carbonated water, citric acid, saccharin, sodium citrate, gum arabic, natural and artificial flavorings, brominated vegetable oil, salt, artificial coloring and 1/20 of 1% benzoate of soda, and stannous chloride as a preservative.

Contains less than 0.04 of 1% saccharin, non–nutritive artificial sweetener which should be used only by persons who must restrict their intake of ordinary sweets; no fats or proteins, 0.03 of 1% available carbohydrates: 1/4 calorie per fluid ounce.

BURRY'S DIPPY CANOES
43¢ Net Wt. 5½ oz.

Ingredients: Degerminated yellow corn meal and corn flour, vegetable oil, oat flour, salt, sugar, soda, certified artificial color and BHA to preserve freshness.

Also: CORN SKIS   43¢ Net Wt. 4½ oz.
SALTY SURFERS 43¢ Net Wt. 7 oz.

Fresca and the Quaker Oats Company snack treats are not singled out for any other purpose than to illustrate a whole growing class of foods. Note, however, that someone must be willing to pay for a little degerminated corn meal, vegetable oil, etc. at a rate of $1.25 per pound and more. Certainly a large share of the cost of Dippy Canoes must be accounted for by the cardboard can with metal ends that is used to package the product and the advertising used to promote it.

Some have suggested that prepared foods should be required to have labels that give not only the ingredients but also the proportions of each. We may be closer to this than we think. Peruse the labels on the pet food shelf in your local supermarket. Apparently we care more about the composition of our dog food than we do about what is in our own food:

GAINES BURGERS (Dogfood)
89¢ Net Wt. 36 Oz.

Ingredients: Beef By–Products and Beef, Soy

Grits, Sucrose, Soybean Meal, Propylene Glycol,
Monocalcium Phosphate, Flaked Soybean Hulls
2.0%, Animal Fat preserved with BHA, Dried
Whey–Product, Iodized Salt 1.2%, Mono and
Di–Glycerides preserved with BHA and citric
acid in propylene glycol, Calcium Carbonate,
Chicken By–Products, Potassium Sorbate, Vitamin E Supplement, Riboflavin Supplement, Vitamin A Supplement, Artificial Coloring, Garlic Powder, D–Activated Plant Sterol,
Cobalt Sulfate, Thiamine Hydrochloride.

GUARANTEED ANALYSIS:

Crude Protein ....Not less than 20.0%
Crude Fat ....Not less than 7.0%
Crude Fiber ....Not more than 3.0%
Ash ....Not more than 7.5%
Moisture ....Not more than 30.0%

VITAMINS AND MINERALS:

Not less than:

Vitamin A ....2500 USP units per lb.
Vitamin D_2 ....750 USP units per lb.
Thiamine ....2 mg per lb.
Riboflavin ....2 mg per lb.
Niacin ....6 mg per lb.
Pyridoxine ....0.6 mg per lb.
D-Pantothenic Acid ....3 mg per lb.
Calcium (Ca) ....1.0 %
Phosphorus (P) ....0.8 %
Iron (Fe) ....0.017 %
Copper (Cu) 0.0008%

Potentially Dangerous Food Additives

It isn't possible to make a complete listing of all of the
food additives that one is likely to see on food labels and
to pass judgment on each one in a book as general as this
handbook. In fact, much of the information that one
would need simply is not known. New information is

bringing new problems to light each year. Witness the furor over cyclamates, saccharin, monosodium glutamate, brominated vegetable oils, and others that has erupted over the past year.

However, it is possible to keep tabs on developments in some. A list of a few of the controversial materials still around follows.

TABLE 33. SUSPECT ADDITIVES

Caffeine. Widely met in coffee, tea, colas, chocolate, and a large variety of drugs (*e.g.,* Anacin, Excedrin, Bromo Seltzer, Neo-Synephrine, No–Doz). Produces mutations in *E. coli* bacteria and chromosome breaks in fruit flies and in cultured human cancer cells. Apparently doesn't do this in mice. The effect in man is not known.

Non-nutritive sweeteners. Non-nutritive because they resist digestion. Thus, they must be eliminated by the body and excreted or hang around.

Cyclamates. Widely used (17 million pounds in 1968) in diet foods and soft drinks until banned in late 1969 because it caused bladder tumors in rats. Also considered to cause chromosome breaks in rat germinal cells. Was GRAS. Not completely off the market.

Saccharin. Still GRAS (generally regarded as safe) but under investigation. Some experiments indicate it causes urinary bladder carcinomas in mice. Diet drinks that use it usually bear the message "should be used only by persons who must restrict their intake of ordinary sweets."

Glycine. Used to cut the bitter aftertaste of saccharin. FDA has given 180 days notice (from late May 1970) that, barring convincing evidence that it is safe, it will be taken off the GRAS list.

Brominated Vegetable Oils. Were used to introduce artificial flavors into soft drinks, and to stabilize orange juice, ice cream and bakery products. FDA removed them from the GRAS list in January 1970 (with 180 days to reformulate products to allowable levels) on the basis of evidence that they cause heart lesions and impaired heart functions in rats.

Nitrites. A meat preservative widely used in pork and fish products, sausages, frankfurters, corned beef, ham—even baby foods. Can be used as a color fixative to keep non–fresh meat looking fresh. A potent mutagen that is commonly used by bacteriologists to chemically alter bacterial and viral DNA. Could cause cancers under the acid conditions in the stomach or react with amines to produce bad things. Restricted in some European countries.
Note: nitrates are similar preservatives, possibly converted to nitrites in the body.

Monosodium Glutamate (MSG). Sold directly as a flavor enhancer and widely used as an additive. Nearly universal in prepared foods such as canned soups, products containing meat, and prepared Chinese foods. Used without being listed on the label in some mayonnaises, French dressings, and salad dressings. Covers up the blandness caused by food processing and storage. Linked with "Chinese restaurant syndrome" which is characterized by headaches, numbness, burning sensations, and sweating. Experiments have indicated brain damage and other deleterious effects in mice. Many feel that it should be banned as an additive. A National Research Council report recently cleared its use in moderate amounts in adult foods but suggested it not be used in baby foods.

For an interesting discussion of such foods as cereals, peanuts and peanut butter, food fats and oils, milk, cheese, baby foods, coffee, fruit juices, and fruit drinks, see the *Consumer Bulletin Annual, 1970*. This also discusses food standards and grades.

In general, it is probably wise to avoid those foods that are heavily dosed with additives. Anything that is labeled *'imitation,'* anything that is highly processed, and anything designed to require a long shelf life is likely to fall into this class of foods. On the other hand, fresh fruits and vegetables and large cuts of meat (not ground meats, canned meats, or processed meats such as sausage) are likely to be free of adulteration.

The defensive diet

There are lots of alternatives to commercially prepared, chemically laden foods.

■ Instead of frozen or canned fruit juices, have the real thing. Eat an orange or grapefruit for breakfast.

■ Instead of a bottle of soda pop, make your own lemonade. Squeeze a lemon and add water and sugar to taste.

■ If it's a diet drink you crave, try the ultimate (zero calories)—water on crushed ice.

If the situation with intentional additives is not good, the problem with unintentional additives is even worse. To protect yourself from pesticide residues in food, you can do the following:

■ Eat low on the food chain. This means a diet of fruits and vegetables and fruits primarily.

■ Wash all fruit and vegetables before you eat them. Some say that the skins of fruit like apples should not be eaten to avoid sprays, but this is also where some of the vitamins are concentrated.

■ Be willing to accept fruit and produce that is less than perfect. A blemish is certainly preferable to a load of poison. Some shoppers actually look for non–perfect produce because they consider it less likely to be laden with pesticides.

■ Grow your own food without pesticides, or buy from organic food stores.

■ Never eat food that has been harvested soon after being sprayed, even if the spray contains only "short–lived" chemicals.

■ If farmers in your area sow seed treated with mercurial fungicides, any wild game you shoot may not be safe to eat. Avoid eating them.

■ Don't eat fish that comes from inland waters unless you know the source to be unpolluted. Even a mountain stream can be contaminated by aerial spraying of a forest upstream.

■ Reduce your consumption of the fat parts of meat, also animal fats in milk, butter, and eggs, for these are the places where the persistent hydrocarbon insecticides tend to be concentrated.

■ Of course, you should never use any pesticide around food. Exposure to pesticides by this route can render insignificant all other sources.

The pesticide residues that men and women carry in the fat of their bodies is acquired by eating pesticide–laden foods over a long period of time. In fact, since the residues can cross the placental barrier, even newborn babies start out with DDT in their bodies. You will not be able to eliminate pesticides from your diet altogether because contamination is so widespread, but a low–pesticide diet will, over the long run, lower the charge of pesticide residues your body has to carry.

Note: It is possible for nursing mothers to have their milk tested for DDT, but the cost is high (about $20). The advantages derived from breastfeeding probably outweigh the dangers of pesticide residues in mothers' milk.

The only sensible overall strategy to adopt is one that tries to end man's insane reliance on pesticides.

Baby foods

Baby foods are worthy of special note. There is mounting concern over several of the substances that have become standard additives in the foods we feed to very small children. As food prices have gone up, baby food manufacturers have turned to adding sugar and starch as a means of keeping the price down. As a result, baby foods have, according to several eminent nutritionists, become less nourishing. There is concern that the sugar contributes to unhealthy baby fat and that it might be a major contributor to the establishment of the American sweet tooth.

The starch that the baby food companies add is not natural, because their baby foods become watery if the child's saliva gets a chance to work on the food in a partially eaten jar. The starch is therefore chemically modified to resist digestion by saliva.

It is hardly surprising that such food tastes bland. To counteract this, monosodium glutamate and salt are added. The catch is that the very young child doesn't have the ability to discriminate by taste. Thus, the main purpose of the additives is to make the food more palatable to the mother, not the baby. They may do more than that. There is concern that the MSG may cause brain damage and that the salt might contribute to hypertension later in life. It should be added that public pressure has moved most baby food manufacturers to remove MSG from their products.

When added to the statistic that packaging represents about one third of the cost of a bottle of baby food, however, the evidence cited above suggests that home preparation of baby food in the blender is a good idea.

10.   COSMETICS AND TOILETRIES

10. Cosmetics and Toiletries

Your own body is, of course, the most intimate part of your environment, and the consumer decisions that have the most direct effect on your body are the ones that you make about cosmetics and toiletries. The story that should be told about this aspect of consumer problems is far too long to be related in this book in anything more than brief outline. In terms of consumer safety, regulatory effort, advertising, and packaging, cosmetics and toiletries has to be the greatest overall disaster area.

As long as no medical claims are made on the package, no pre–testing is required by existing law to check the safety of a cosmetic formulation, much less its effectiveness. In such cases the Food and Drug Administration even lacks the power to require any statement of contents on the label.

At the same time, cosmetics are formulated with a variety of compounds which are known to be dangerous. Strong allergic reactions are not uncommon, for example, against the coal tar dyes that are used in most permanent hair colorants. These have been known to cause blindness and even death when used in eyelash preparations. Hexachlorophene, a common bacteriostat used in soaps and a wide range of medicated and unmedicated products, can sensitize the skin and cause violent allergic reactions. There is also concern over the use of hormones in skin creams, the regular use of alcohol–based mouthwashes, and the metallic dyes used in other permanent hair colorants.

Medicated cosmetics and do–it–yourself treatment can aggravate a bad medical situation and keep the user from consulting a physician when he should. Such medication applied trick–or–treat fashion can be bad for you.

In terms of advertising, the industry has succeeded in creating the consumer mentality it wants and which it exploits to the fullest. By encouraging throughout the population an acute awareness of bad breath, dandruff, body odors, blemishes, aging, and obesity, and at the same time holding out tantalizing solutions to these problems with rewards of sexual fulfillment, perfect bodies, social acceptance, and youth, the industry has indoctrinated the public to use cosmetics. Women have been the particular targets of this exploitation.

The industry's efforts in packaging are unsurpassed in terms of excess. The following figures from the 1969 annual report of Fabergé, Incorporated and Subsidiaries, indicate the relative importance that a leader in the industry puts on testing and promotion:

Net Sales	$140,201,507	100.0%
Advertising and promotion	$17,892,249	12.8%
Research and development	$417,916	0.3%

THE BODY IS AN ECOSYSTEM

Considering the body as an ecosystem is an instructive point of view to take when assessing the worth of cosmetics and the validity of their advertising claims. For the most part, cosmetics and toiletries are concerned with the surface of your body, the skin. Yet it is important to remember that what goes on inside the body has an important effect on what happens on the surface.

Many problems that are dealt with cosmetically are actually manifestations of dietary inadequacies, hormone imbalances brought on by puberty or emotional stress, or medical problems. In such cases cosmetics and toiletries tend to deal only with the symptoms and not the causes.

Consider the ecology of the skin. The skin is composed of layers, the outermost of which is continually flaking off. As this happens the skin produces sweat and oils, and these feed rather large populations of microorganisms. Where there are more hair follicles and sweat glands (and more nutrients) there are more microorganisms. Bacteria predominate. In the healthy armpit there are typically 15.5 million bacteria per square inch! On the back, the number is about 2000 per square inch. It should be emphasized that this is a normal and healthy situation.

As in any ecosystem, problems tend to arise when there is a change in the host environment—a failure to keep yourself clean or a dietary or emotional crisis. Then bacteria and fungi can take advantage of the momentary imbalance to gain a foothold. Normally the harmful organisms would be unable to dislodge the beneficial populations.

THE PRODUCTS

The following partial listing of cosmetics and toiletries includes some advice that the cosmetics industry won't give you.

Soaps. The keystone of a cosmetic program is the soap. Specialized deodorant soaps such as Dial with hexachlorophene are unnecessary. In fact, by attacking the normal bacterial population of the skin, such products can open up an ecological niche for undesirable bacteria in much the same manner that using pesticides tends to disrupt stable ecosystems. Use a soap that is free of chemicals that pollute the skin.

Skin creams. Skin creams can restore the balance of oils to a dry skin after washing. However, the extravagant claims made for some creams—wrinkle removers and skin restorers—are usually patently false. The manufacturers periodically introduce their newest incarnation of preparations containing royal jelly from bees, hormones, placental or embroyo extract, shark or turtle oil, and vitamin A, promote the product with enormous ad campaigns, and sell it until the effect of the advertising wears off. In general, preparations that try to feed the skin by spreading junk on the surface stand little chance of doing much good because the skin is a very effective barrier to the passage of anything into the body. It takes its nourishment from within.

Using creams instead of soaps is not considered to be a very good idea, especially if you have an acne problem, for it tends to add to the problem of clogged pores. The proper cure involves control of diet and regular washing of the skin to remove the plugs from the openings of the affected glands. Medicated soaps containing sulfur, resorcinol, and salicylic acid are considered to be helpful in peeling off superficial layers of the skin, but they should be used under the supervision of a doctor. Remedies based on the germ theory—attacking the acne bacillus—do not attack the real cause, and thus do very little good.

Shampoos. Dandruff is a normal condition of the scalp, produced as the outermost layers of the skin slough off. The situation on the scalp is different from the rest of the body in that the scalp is especially oily and the flakes of skin tend to be larger and more visible. Little is known about the mechanism that causes excess dandruff and so most of the treatments are little more than empirical. The best advice if you have dandruff is to shampoo more frequently and if that doesn't work, to consult a dermatologist.

Hair dyes and rinses. The hazards involved in use of the two common permanent hair colorants have been mentioned briefly. The coal tar dyes or oxidation dyes are by far the most dangerous. It is wise to apply a bit of the product you plan to use to a patch of skin behind your ear or in the crook of the elbow for a day before each use to test for an adverse reaction. The temporary dyes tend to be made from vegetable colorants and seem to be relatively safe.

Deodorants. Underarm odors are usually caused by bacterial action on sweat and oils that are allowed to remain on the skin for a relatively long time. Deodorants usually attack the bacteria with some sort of chemical agent or merely try to cover up the odor with something more pleasant. The way to get at the cause of the problem is to bathe more frequently. It should also be noted that not all body odors are as offensive as the manufacturers of deodorants and colognes would have us believe.

Antiperspirants. Attacking the problem by inhibiting the natural sweating of the skin, they interfere with a natural eliminative process.

Mouthwashes. Bad breath is not caused primarily by bacteria. For some people the problem is metabolic—that is, their own body chemistry produces odors that make their breath smell bad. In the case of odors from onions, the odor comes not from the mouth itself but from the lungs by way of the blood stream and the intestines where the odor is absorbed from the food. In cases where odor does come from bacterial action on food particles that have been left in the mouth, a simple brushing of the teeth is more effective than using a mouthwash. The main effect of mouthwashes is simply to mask the odor.

WHAT YOU CAN DO

As an environmentalist there are several factors in addition to effectiveness that you should consider:

■ Most cosmetics and toiletries are terribly overpackaged. Try to select brands that are least offensive in this respect.

■ Some brands use ingredients that come from animals that are threatened by extinction. Whale oil soaps are a case in point. A whole line of turtle oil cosmetics has been given a large promotion by a well-known actress. Avoid both types of products by all means. The whales and turtles that supply the ingredients are far too scarce to use them for such a trivial purpose.

that not all body odor areas originate in the mammary ducts of deodorants and cosmetics, would have us believe. Anyone sprayed, sprinkling the problem by inhibiting the natural showing of the skin, they interfere with a natural eliminative process.

Withal unseen, that means is not caused primarily by bacteria. For some people the problem of metabolic—that is, they come of body chemistry problems often that others don't even smell bad. In the case of odors from patients, the odor comes not from the mouth itself but from the lungs by way of the blood stream and the tongue where the odor is different from the teeth or even where odor does come from bacterial action on food particles that have been in all in the mouth a couple hours. The teeth is more effective than using a mouthwash.

The main effect of mouthwashes is simply, in most of the odors.

WHAT YOU CAN DO

As an encouragement that there are several facts in addition to effectiveness that you should consider.

Many cosmetics and toiletries are terribly overpackaged. Try to select brands that are least expensive in this respect.

Some brands use ingredients that come from animals that are threatened by extinction. Whale oil soaps are a case in point. A whole line of turtle oil cosmetics has itself given a large promotion for a well-known cause. Avoid both types of products by all means. The whales and turtles that supply the ingredients are far too scarce to use them for such a trivial purpose.

11. BIRTH, LIVING, AND DEATH

11. Birth, Living, and Death

Most of the topics discussed in this chapter are controversial. Many of them involve medical and moral issues. Rather than try to be comprehensive or to resolve the controversies, we will simply lay out some of the options and consider them from one point of view.

POPULATION AND THE QUALITY OF LIFE

A great debate has developed over the question of how much of the "blame" for the deteriorating quality of our environment should be assigned to too–many–people and how much to failures of our social systems and technology. On the one hand is the faction that tends to trace most of the problems to the simple fact that more and more people are putting demands on our planet's finite resources. On the other is the group which finds solutions to most of our problems in technology and social engineering. They do not feel that we have reached the limits that the finite earth imposes, and tend to ascribe our problems to weaknesses in our social, industrial, and governmental structures which can be fixed.

The differences of the two points of view are important primarily because of the different sorts of solutions that their proponents propose. The weakness of both positions is that advocates of each tend to spend unfortunately large quantities of time and energy defending their point of view *against* the other—birth control *versus* technical solutions.

Rather than take sides in this sterile debate, this book adopts the ecologically sound posture that both sides are right and that the only course of action that makes sense is to adopt those strategies from either side which point toward survival in a better world.

You can make your personal contribution to survival by reducing your consumption, by taking care of your wastes, and by using only those products that are compatible with other parts of the environment. The sum of all of your little actions will be significant. At the same time you can make a major contribution to reducing the demand on our finite resources by limiting the size of your family.

While society's goal is not to limit the number of children that any one couple has to two, its interest is clearly in controlling the rate of growth of the population so that the country can live within the limits of its resource base and the capabilities of its social institutions—something which the United States now fails to do. The family that willingly has large numbers of children is clearly placing a large burden on society—a morally reprehensible act. Either others must forego having children or the collective load is increased. In this respect, families that can "afford" many children tend to be the worst offenders: for their children, raised affluently, will consume more and waste more than the average.

From a personal point of view, controlling the number of children that you have has the advantage that each child is more likely to be wanted and the economic burden of raising the child can be planned for.

Stop at two

There is a large number of contraceptive techniques. They range from abstinence, the rhythm method, and *coitus interruptus*—which depend on will power and are less than sure—to the use of the condom, diaphragm, intrauterine device (IUD), spermicide foam or jelly, and the pill. Abortion is beginning to be recognized as an acceptable method of terminating unwanted pregnancy when contraceptive methods have failed to prevent it. And sterilization—vasectomy for the male, or tubal ligation for the female—is the method of choice for a growing number of people after their family has reached its planned size.

The method of birth control that is used should be a personal decision made by the husband and wife. It is also a medical matter, and a doctor should be consulted whenever a medical method is used. In practice, church and state also impose conditions that restrict the freedom of the couple to decide for themselves. But attitudes are rapidly changing. The Roman Catholic church is no longer monolithic in its opposition to any form of birth control. Many individual catholics consider the question to be a matter of personal conscience. And nowhere are conditions changing more rapidly than on the question of abortion. It is interesting to note that in Japan abortion is the socially acceptable method of controlling births and the IUD and the pill are socially unacceptable: whereas in this country, the situation is precisely reversed.

The reader who wishes to have more information on any particular method of birth control is referred to *The Birth Control Handbook,* available from the McGill Students' Society, 3480 McTavish Street, Montreal, Quebec, Canada—or any other reputable manual on marriage and birth control. Your doctor is another source of information. In addition, such organizations as Planned Parenthood, Women's Liberation, and student groups can supply information that is relevant to your locale.

Adopt the rest

If you want to have a large family, adopt one. There are thousands of children who need the love that you can give. Investigate to find out whether you qualify to adopt a child. In some states single adults, as well as married couples, can adopt. Ask friends who have adopted, investigate through your church, or state and municipal social agencies. If you are unsuccessful in finding a suitable agency, contact the Adoption Resource Exchange of North America, 44 East 23rd Street, New York, New York 10010.

POLLUTION AND HEALTH

The extent to which pollution affects your health is not fully understood, but it is clear that the effects are major.

Carcinogens contaminate our air and food, teratogenic pesticide residues deform fetuses, mutagens attack the genetic information we pass on to our children. Residues of chemicals that are used to protect our crops, additives that are used in our foods, and cosmetics we apply to our own bodies pose threats to health that are poorly researched and poorly understood.

Unfortunately there isn't much that you can do to protect yourself against many types of pollution. In some cases the only thing you can do is run. This is what a growing number of residents of such large cities as New York and Los Angeles have had to do. Although pollution *is* everywhere there are still some areas that are relatively clear of it.

This will not continue to be the case, however, if everyone merely tries to flee pollution. We must stop and fight. The pollution that you generate will harm someone else if it doesn't harm you. Protect yourself from self-inflicted pollution.

■ Don't use pesticides. Home exposure is dangerous and unnecessary.

■ Take all due precautions when using any hazardous product. Avoid them whenever possible.

■ Don't go overboard with cosmetics or prepared foods.

■ Don't smoke. It attacks your own body and pollutes the air others must breathe.

■ Eat healthful foods and keep yourself in shape by exercise.

DEATH

The American way of death is as unecological as the American way of life. Rather than recycle our bodies back to the earth—from dust to dust—we embalm them. The blood is replaced by a chemical solution to preserve the semblance of life in an elaborate coffin. Cemeteries are monuments to this folly.

12. CLOTHING

12. Clothing

When you think about the relationship between clothing and the environment, probably the first thing that comes to mind is the use of furs and skins that come from endangered species of animals. While this is a significant problem, the great majority of people will never buy a leopard coat or an alligator purse.

PESTICIDES AND COTTON

Everyone, however, wears cotton. Does cotton pollute? You bet it does. Cotton farmers use 70 percent of the DDT, 69 percent of the toxaphene, 86 percent of the endrin, and 80 percent of the methyl parathion—all either deadly and/or persistent—to combat insect pests that attack their crop. Cotton accounts for the use of more than half of the total amount of pesticides used. Furthermore, as pests evolve a resistance to the commonly used pesticides, pressures build to introduce new and potentially more dangerous agents. For instance, introduction of Azodrin on cotton crops in the San Joaquin Valley in California in 1967 was accompanied by disastrous wildlife kills and one of the lowest yields of cotton in the decade.

In addition to insecticides, defoliants are used to facilitate cotton harvesting.

The hollowness of the federal government's recent move to "ban" all but "essential" uses of DDT is made clear by the fact that use of the persistent pesticide on cotton has been interpreted as being "essential." But the DDT that goes onto a cotton field ends up killing the same natural predators and poisoning the milk of the same mothers as the "nonessential" use does.

The cotton industry's addiction to pesticides is not necessary—at least not on the scale that the U.S. Department of Agriculture seems willing to sanction today. Biological controls for cotton acreage have been used successfully on a small scale in the Coachella Valley in California. But until U.S.D.A. wakes up to its responsibility to the long–range welfare of humanity, pesticides will continue to be a part of the environmental cost of every cotton shirt and calico dress.

MOTHPROOFING

It is doubtful whether any of the pesticides that are applied to the cotton crop survive the processing of the fiber that goes along with clothing manufacture. They don't have to. Apparently it has been common practice to use persistent pesticides as a method of permanently mothproofing garments that have been dry-cleaned. A survey of 41 dry–cleaning firms in Mississippi in 1968 revealed that 25 of them used mothproofing agents.

> "When mothproofing agents were employed, it was generally the practice to mix a quantity of the agent with the regular dry cleaning fluid. Thus, in these firms, every article of clothing which was dry-cleaned was mothproofed as well, regardless of whether the customer had requested mothproofing. Four main mothproofing chemicals were used: Sanex, Milo, Tripruf, and Sanitone. All four products contained DDT, although Sanitone, which was 100 percent DDT, was the only product in which the DDT concentration was identified."
>
> —*Mrak Commission Report on Pesticides and Their Relationship to Environmental Health.*

WOOL

Wool is another natural fiber that has an environmental cost. Although the cost is nothing so dramatic as the use of poison, wool-growing does tie up a considerable quantity of land and water just in raising the sheep that produce the wool. In many cases the land actually used for this purpose is marginal and cannot be considered to have been removed from agricultural use. However, the fact remains that growing wool is a very inefficient use of resources. It is disturbing that one should think in such terms, but given the ever-growing world demands on resources, such considerations become inevitable.

SYNTHETIC FIBERS

The advent of rayon and nylon heralded a grand menagerie of synthetic fibers and modified natural fibers that today have taken over 38 percent of the total fibers market. The trend is unmistakably toward more synthetics and less natural fibers. What this means to the environment is not clear at present.

Of the fibers now used, 17 percent are cellulosic. That is, they are based on the natural plant fiber material cellulose. Another 21 percent are totally synthetic—polyesters, polyamides, polyacrylics—and these are derived from chemicals that come out of the petroleum and chemicals

TABLE 34. TEXTILE FIBER CONSUMPTION

	Total consumption (Billions of pounds)	Per capita consumption (Pounds) All fibers	Man-made
1960	6.49	36.2	9.9
1965	8.49	45.0	18.3
1970	10.50	50.9	31.0
1975	12.50	56.0	40.0
1980	15.60	64.0	48.0

Note: This includes all markets for textiles of which clothing is about 40 percent today. Home furnishings (rugs, etc.) and automotive uses (tires, etc.) are other major users of textiles.

Source: *Chemical & Engineering News*, April 20, 1970.

industries. Since the factories that manufacture the chemical fibers also pollute, it isn't clear whether synthetic fibers are a better alternative to the pesticide–laden cotton fields or a worse one.

All fibers, regardless of their origin, pass through the textile industry on their way to becoming clothes or fabrics. Although the textile industry ranks below food manufacturing, paper, and metals as a source of water pollution, individual plants are very bad polluters. Washing the fibers and cloth, and bleaching, dyeing, and cleaning them uses large quantities of water and dumps lots of detergents, dyes, and other chemicals into our waterways.

In positive terms, the introduction of synthetic fibers and the new modifications of natural fibers have facilitated the use of permanent dyes and the introduction of such innovations as permanent press and soil repellancy. The decrease in ironing alone has probably saved many millions of kilowatt–hours of electricity.

DISPOSABLE CLOTHING

Part of the reason why clothing doesn't cause more pollution is because it is basically a durable good. We buy it to last for a period of many months or years and so it doesn't involve the overuse of many resources in its production.

The introduction of disposable clothing could change all of this. Disposable diapers seem to be taking over a significant portion of the market, and International Paper has introduced us to the disposable bikini. Paper dresses are already a reality. These are developments that should be resisted strongly on purely environmental grounds. Don't follow along. The costs to the environment of having to produce a largely disposable wardrobe and then to dispose of it are simply too great.

Instead, try to make your clothes last. Buy clothes that will wear well. Alter your clothing instead of discarding it.

Don't throw away clothing that someone else could use. Pass it on to a friend or a relative, or donate it to someone or some institution that deals in used clothing.

Learn how to make your own clothing. Not only will it save you money, it can be a fun way to put your creative abilities to work.

FASHION

If one were to carry the ecological arguments to their logical extreme, we would all be wearing uniforms, durably constructed of the least–polluting and most readily washable material. Clearly this is not reasonable. But if you carry clothing design to the other extreme, you have the fashion industry. Buying a wardrobe that becomes obsolete in a year is clearly not very reasonable either.

Resist their "advice," for the fashion industry would make women, and men too, slaves to the dictates of the fashion "experts" who, of course, are employed by the industry. Instead, buy clothes that make you look attractive.

A word about the ecological factors that should be considered in the mini versus midi versus maxi controversy—clearly mini is favored because it requires considerably less cloth. In the winter, however, the maxi would be preferable because it keeps the wearer warm and would reduce general heating requirements.

Dress coolly in the summer and warmly in the winter. If wearing a sweater in your home during the winter will keep you comfortable with the thermostat a degree or two lower, wear one. You can reduce your consumption of fuel by five to ten percent or more.

ENDANGERED SPECIES

Fashion has had a lot to do with the deaths of whole species of animals. For example, the fact that the strainer teeth of the baleen whale were used for a long time in corsets and bustles was very unhealthy for the whales.

Thousands of birds have been slaughtered for their feathers alone. Today the primary concern is over the big cats and other animals that are being killed for their furs and skins.

Do not make a personal contribution to the extinction of any species now endangered. It is important that they be preserved to protect animal diversity, for scientific study, and for purely esthetic reasons. Man–made pollution, invasion of their habitat, and illegal sport hunting are threatening enough to many of these species without adding the demand that exotic fashions can create. Boycott leopard coats, polar bear rugs, and alligator shoes, boots, belts, and handbags.

What are the exotic fashions of the future going to use? Marian Christy, an award–winning fashion critic with *The Boston Globe,* points out one new direction: "While the alligators are being coddled, fashionables will have to switch to a new batch of skins which promise to be the 'in' leathers of the 1970s. Frog, ostrich, elephant and anteater are new substitutes for alligator." Frogs are probably all right, but if you are an anteater or an elephant, watch out.

Boycott alone will never be enough protection because it will never be 100% effective, and as long as there is a market, animals that shouldn't be killed will be. Thus, the new legislative steps that are aimed at international and interstate shipment of skins or directly at the sale of certain products are very important. A proposed New York law would ban the sale of skins of the following animals in that state:

snow leopards	alligators	polar bears
clouded leopards	caimans	cougars
leopards	crocodiles	jaguars
tigers	vicuñas	ocelots
cheetahs	red wolves	margays

A new federal law banning the sale of products made from the skins of animals near extinction goes into effect in September 1970. Like other regulatory legislation, the ultimate effect of these legislative measures will depend on enforcement.

Other ways to help

Car Pools and Offering Rides 284
Make Your Second Car a Bicycle 285
Walk 286

Table 35. Pollution Production and Fuel
Consumption by Different Modes of
Transportation 254
Table 36. Automobile Emissions 263
Table 37. 1968 Federal Emissions Standards 264
Table 38. Failure of Cars to Meet Federal
Standards 264
Table 39. Union Oil Performance Tests* 266

***How Class winners were decided—Union Oil Performance Tests**

The cars were divided into nine classes and competed only against other cars in their class.

The car that was best in any one test was awarded a score of 100%. The other cars were scored according to how they compared to the winner. *Example:* If car A was tops in fuel economy with 10 miles per gallon it would receive a score of 100%. Car B totaled 8.4 miles per gallon and received an 84% score. Car C with 7.34 miles per gallon scored 73.4%. The overall class winner was the car whose average percentage for all three events was the highest.

The First Trial: Fuel Economy The fuel consumption of each car was determined by driving a precise distance under typical traffic conditions.

Each car circled the Daytona International Speedway road course exactly 5 times. During each lap, a car had to maintain an average speed of 40 mph except for a "speed zone" in which it had to be traveling 65 mph. A car also had to come to a complete stop once on each lap. This routine closely simulated the effects of normal driving on gas consumption.

For this test, the car's regular fuel system was closed off. It was then fitted with a sealed canister of premium or regular 76 gasoline, depending on the engine's specifications. Highly-sensitive scales weighed every canister to the closest 1/10th of a gram before and after the run. The difference in weight was translated into the miles-per-gallon consumption rate of each car entered in the trials.

The Second Trial: Acceleration The Trials also measured the time each new car took to accelerate from 25 mph—a normal occurrence when entering expressways or passing on highways. To do this accurately, every car was fitted with special portable electronic timing equipment.

A test car started a run by cruising at just under 25 mph. It was then given a signal to accelerate as fast as possible to 70 mph. An electronic clock started when the car hit exactly 25 mph, and stopped at exactly 70 mph. Speeds weren't taken from dashboard speedometers but were determined by a "fifth wheel" attached to the rear of each car.

A car made two runs on the same course, one in each direction, to minimize the effects of any wind. The official time was the average of both runs.

The Third Trial: Braking This test measured a car's ability to come to a complete stop from 65 mph in a single traffic lane. Before the test, each car warmed up its brakes to simulate the effects of normal driving.

Depending on the car's class, it was required to make a specified number of warm-up stops from 70 mph. These were gradual stops to a specified rate of deceleration, to produce the effects of normal stop-and-go driving.

For the actual test, each driver speeded up to at least 65 mph. When he entered the test course, he applied his brakes. An electronic marker attached to a rear-riding fifth wheel marked the exact spot where the car came to a dead stop. This duplicates a highway emergency stop situation.

If any of the pylons which border the 12-foot lane were knocked down, or the test car infringed on any other rules, penalties were assessed.

13. Transportation:
Where Does It Get Us?

The following information is excerpted from a pamphlet entitled *"America's Lifelines,"* published by the U.S. Department of Transportation:

America's highways now are being used at better than a trillion–miles–a–year mark. It is difficult to comprehend the enormity of such usage. Statistics tell part of the story: More than 100 million drivers operated nearly 100 million vehicles (82.8 million automobiles and 17.1 million trucks) over 3.7 million miles of roads and streets in 1968, traveling some 1 trillion 10 billion vehicle miles.

There is a vehicle for every 2.1 persons in the United States; 26 vehicles for every mile of road; a mile of road for each square mile of land. Four of every five people old enough to drive have a driver's license. The figures grow bigger each year. . . .

The Interstate System is a spectacular undertaking. The average mile costs around $1,400,000, with the average in rural areas fixed at about $887,000, and in urban areas at $4,000,000 a mile.

The pavement of the System, if put into one huge parking lot, would be 20½ miles square and over half of the motor vehicles in the U.S. could be parked on it. New right–of–way needed amounts to 1.8 million acres. Total excavation will move enough dirt and rock to blanket Connecticut knee–deep. Sand, gravel, and

crushed stone for the construction would build a
mound 50 feet wide and 9 feet high completely
around the world. The concrete used would
build six sidewalks to the moon; the tar and
asphalt would build driveways for 35 million
homes. The steel will take 30 million tons of
iron ore, 18 million tons of coal, and 6½ million tons of limestone. The culvert and drain
pipe required equals the quantity used in the
combined water and sewer–main systems in six
cities the size of Chicago.

Typical interstate rural highway construction
requires 9 times as much excavation work as
the main road of a generation ago, 7 times as
much tar and asphalt, and 4½ times as much
cement, 3½ times as much aggregate, and 3½
times as much steel.

The total cost of the Interstate System will be in the
neighborhood of $75 billion when completed. Money is
being spent at the rate of $4 billion per year to see
the system through to completion. When it is done, it
will comprise little more than 1 percent of the nation's
total road and street mileage, but will carry 20 percent
of the nation's traffic.

In a typical government–style cost–benefit analysis, the
average Federal tax payments to the Highway Trust Fund
are figured to be about $30 a year for an automobile while
the benefits for the automobile should be about $100 a
year. But what are the costs and benefits to people?

The following information is excerpted from a pamphlet distributed by Free Wheel, a Cambridge, Massachusetts, group:

The automobile is destroying our communities, our land, our atmosphere, and our very
lives. It is both a symptom and a cause of the
competitive and privatized lifestyle which infects
us all. It has become one of the most powerful

tools of psychic manipulation and consumer en-
slavement.

60,000 people die every year in automobile
accidents. Another 170,000 are permanently
maimed and almost 3½ million are injured. Exhaust fumes choke our breathing and burn our
eyes. Entire species of trees and food plants are
exterminated by rising levels of auto pollutants.
Untold acres are paved over by new superhigh-
ways and vast parking lots, permanently dis-
rupting the ground water system and ruining
our precious remaining parks and recreational
spaces.

Our older cities, built originally for walking
and face-to-face contact, are torn down to
meet the demands of the automobile. Downtown
areas are filled up with high rise garages, which
become giant pollution generators at rush hours
and remain inactive and devoid of humanity the
rest of the day. The poorest families are pushed
out of their homes and what community they
have is torn apart to make way for new expressways.

In our newer communities, any form of transportation other than the automobile has been
rendered impossible. Walking is out of the question; all possible destinations are too far and too
scattered. Even a quart of milk may require a
two mile trip by car to the nearest sprawling
shopping center. Public transportation is virtually non-existent. In such a community, only
a car can save a person from complete isola-
tion.

The social costs of this life style are catastrophic. Life becomes privatized. . . . The automobile cuts us off from other people, allowing
only the most aggressive and hostile interaction
through honking horns and snarling traffic
jams. It may even deprive us of contact with
the earth. People no longer go to the country

to walk the land, to smell the air, to hear the mountain streams; rather they "go for a ride," partaking of the world through their metal picture frame.

While the auto–highway complex has mushroomed, we have allowed our public transportation system to decay, progressively immobilizing four groups who don't have access to autos— the poor, youth, the elderly, women.

In addition to the above, the following facts are relevant to understanding our present system of transportation.

■ In 1963, retail sales of passenger car dealers totaled $40.5 billion (16.5% of the national total), tire, battery, and accessory dealers had sales of $3.3 billion (1.4%), and gasoline service stations $17.8 billion (7.3%).

■ In 1967, 77.7 billion gallons of motor fuel was consumed in the U.S.: 55.3 billion for passenger cars at 671 gallons per car; 0.93 billion for buses at 2,755 gallons per bus; and 21.4 billion for trucks and combinations at 1,324 gallons per vehicle. Average mileage for passenger cars was 14.08 miles per gallon. It has been steadily declining since at least 1940. And petroleum pollutes.

■ Transportation uses up about one quarter of the total energy spent.

■ About 9 million vehicles are scrapped each year. A Bureau of Mines study has indicated that in 1965 18% of junk autos were abandoned on public or private property.

■ The automotive contribution to air pollution includes 91% of all carbon monoxide, 63% of unburned hydrocarbons, 48% of oxides of nitrogen, 8% of particulate matter, and 4% of sulfur oxides. Total tonnage is about 90 million tons yearly from automobiles. The automobile accounts for at least 60 percent of the total air pollution in the U.S. and as high as 85 percent in some urban areas.

■ This doesn't count the pollution from the plants that make the cement and asphalt for highways.

■ Carbon monoxide and lead levels in urban air are now commonly far above the recommended maximum limits.

■ Asbestos from brake linings and rubber from tire wear are not widely recognized to be the pollutants that they are. They lodge in your lungs and can induce cancer there.

■ 85% of urban noise originates from internal combustion engines.

■ Average speed in New York in–city traffic is 8.5 mph.

■ One million acres of land are paved each year.

■ Total automobile insurance premiums written in 1967 were $10.8 billion and losses paid $5.8 billion— bodily injury liability $5.0 billion and $2.6 billion paid; property damage liability $2.1 billion and $1.2 billion paid; and physical damage (collision, comprehensive) $3.7 billion and $2.0 billion paid.

■ Automotive claims have badly clogged our courts and have impeded our whole system of justice.

■ Automotive advertising expenditures in 1968 included: $268 million for space in newspapers, exclusive of production costs; $113 million for space in magazines; $73 million for spot television advertising and $125 million for network advertising. Gasoline, lubricants, etc., added $49 million for spots and $36 million for network coverage.

■ In the San Francisco Bay region 83% of the automobile trips take less than 15 minutes.

■ Statistically, the average car load is only 1.2 persons.

YOUR TRANSPORTATION STRATEGY

Because transportation consumes such a large share of the resources you spend, both natural and financial, and because it is such a large contributor to the environmental and social ills that plague modern society, you should put some thought into devising a personal transportation strategy that will work toward a better system.

We are no longer free to take our cars and highways and planes so much for granted.

In the cities

The first step should be to get a vision of what a desirable system might mean. To a great extent, we already know where we should be headed. First, consider urban systems. In terms of efficiency and minimizing pollution, mass transportation is far better than our present reliance on the private auto. Table 35 gives an indication of how much less pollution trains and buses generate per passenger mile and how much less fuel they expend.

Use the table to compare the pollution and fuel consumption of different modes of transportation. For example, if you want to compare taking a trip to a city that is not so far away that time is a determining factor, first select the proper loading factors. If the options are traveling in an old jalopy with two passengers and a driver, taking a half-full bus, a half-full plane, or a half-full train, the options would rank: train (12 gm/100 passenger miles), bus (27), jet (160), and auto (2666) in terms of CO emissions, and so forth.

The figures in the table are generally rather rough approximations. Not all trains, buses, cars, or power plants operate at similar emissions levels. Nor is the mass of emissions the most relevant basis for comparison. For instance, aircraft organics (hydrocarbons) are heavy in aldehydes, which have particularly undesirable effects. Furthermore, some of the pollution is highly concentrated in particular locations—near airports, highways, and the power plants that create the energy to run streetcars. On the basis of pollution and fuel consumption alone, however, trends do emerge. The automobile, even when fully loaded (which it seldom is), is least favorable. Trains and buses pollute the least.

Other calculations show that, in terms of space, a transportation corridor turned over to the highway and automobile moves only 1/17th the number of people that would be moved in the same space by buses and only 1/12th the load that trains would carry.

On a different speed scale, bicycles could move 2.8 times as many people per amount of space. If a bicycler can make 10 miles an hour, the car would have to exceed 28 mph to rack up more passenger miles on the same system of streets. But the New York City average speed for cars during rush hour is only 8.5 mph, 13 mph on the feeder roads. It's a fact that today in many cities you can make better time aboard a bicycle than in a car.

The private automobile spends most of its time unused. Extensive space must be taken up just to provide a stall for the beast. In fact there must be several stalls—at home, office, and shopping center. Schools have been known to rob children of play space to accommodate the teachers' cars. Parking space is almost always paved; this renders it almost useless for anything else, disrupts the groundwater system, and creates flash flood conditions.

On the other hand, mass–transit vehicles spend a much larger proportion of their time in service, and generally need only one parking place. While they may not deliver you to the doorstep of your final destination, neither do they make you walk long distances just because parking spaces are scarce.

In the suburbs

However, not everyone lives in the central city. There, subways, monorails, and bus networks are found, but in the suburbs and the sprawling new suburban cities of California . . . The problem is a very difficult one, and it illustrates the ecological truth that everything is related to everything else. Urban sprawl is very much tied up with the transportation crisis.

Although urban sprawl makes public mass transit more difficult, the possibility need not be ruled out altogether. A network of public transportation corridors could connect the parts of the city, supplemented by a finer network of smaller carriers to service the residential areas. Some experiments are underway with "dial–a–bus" systems that use computers and small, 10–passenger vehicles to provide the ultimate flexibility for such a residential service.

TABLE 35. POLLUTION PRODUCTION AND FUEL CONSUMPTION BY DIFFERENT MODES OF TRANSPORTATION

Figures are quantity per 100 miles or per 100 passenger miles as appropriate.

MODE	Organics	CO	NO_x	Particulates	Fuel	Comments
Automobile (Uncontrolled Emissions)	1100 gm	8000 gm	400 gm	38 gm	6.7 gal	Per vehicle: 15 miles/gal.
	183 gm	1333 gm	67 gm	6 gm	1.1 gal	Per pass. (6 in car)
	220 gm	1600 gm	80 gm	8 gm	1.3 gal	Per pass. (5 in car)
	275 gm	2000 gm	100 gm	10 gm	1.7 gal	Per pass. (4 in car)
	367 gm	2666 gm	133 gm	13 gm	2.2 gal	Per pass. (3 in car)
	550 gm	4000 gm	200 gm	19 gm	3.3 gal	Per pass. (2 in car)
Automobile (At 1971 Calif. Standards)	220 gm	2300 gm	400 gm	38 gm	4.0 gal	Per vehicle: 25 miles/gal.
	37 gm	383 gm	67 gm	6 gm	0.7 gal	Per pass. (6 in car)
	44 gm	460 gm	80 gm	8 gm	0.8 gal	Per pass. (5 in car)
	55 gm	575 gm	100 gm	10 gm	1.0 gal	Per pass. (4 in car)
	73 gm	767 gm	133 gm	13 gm	1.3 gal	Per pass. (3 in car)
	110 gm	1150 gm	200 gm	19 gm	2.0 gal	Per pass. (2 in car)
Boeing 707	3460 gm	10900 gm	5300 gm	9250 gm	375 gal	Per airplane
	27 gm	84 gm	42 gm	71 gm	2.9 gal	Per pass. (130 in plane)
	51 gm	160 gm	78 gm	136 gm	5.5 gal	Per pass. (68 in plane)
Bus (Diesel)	1620 gm	672 gm	1090 gm	1660 gm	20 gal	Per vehicle
	32 gm	13 gm	22 gm	33 gm	0.4 gal	Per pass. (50 in bus)
	65 gm	27 gm	44 gm	65 gm	0.8 gal	Per pass. (25 in bus)
Train (Diesel)	20800 gm	8630 gm	14000 gm	21300 gm	257 gal	Per train
	15 gm	6 gm	10 gm	15 gm	0.2 gal	Per pass. (1400 on train)
	30 gm	12 gm	20 gm	30 gm	0.4 gal	Per pass. (700 on train)
Streetcar (Electric)	620 gm	240 gm	18800 gm	3400 gm	26 gal	Per streetcar
	8 gm	3 gm	235 gm	42 gm	0.3 gal	Per pass. (80 on car)
	31 gm	12 gm	940 gm	170 gm	1.3 gal	Per pass. (20 on car)

Sources: Most of the figures from which this table was derived were obtained from *Handbook of the San Francisco Region* by Robert H. Dreisbach.

Notes: Noteworthy pollutants not listed include lead for automobile operation—to the tune of about 2.4 to 4 grams per gallon of gas. For a car getting 15 mpg. on high octane gas that would be 27 grams per 100 vehicle miles, of which as much as a half gets out into the air. Streetcar emissions are based on the oil needed to generate the electric power. Sulfur dioxide is generated at 66000 gm/100 car miles. Airport noise is also a pollutant. The figures for the Boeing 707 presume 375 gallons of jet fuel per 100 miles of operation and emissions of:

Organics	2.03 lb/100 gal or	3.0 lb/1000 lb fuel
NO_x	3.12 lb/100 gal or	4.6 lb/1000 lb fuel
CO_2	6.4 lb/100 gal or	9.4 lb/1000 lb fuel
Particulates	5.44 lb/100 gal or	8.0 lb/1000 lb fuel

The figures for the bus and the train presume fuel consumption as indicated (about 5 mpg for the bus). Emissions per quantity of diesel fuel are considered to be the same for the two engines:

Organics	17.8 lb/100 gal or	16.2 gm/mile (bus)
NO_x	12 lb/100 gal or	10.9 gm/mile (bus)
CO	7.4 lb/100 gal or	6.7 gm/mile (bus)
Particulates	18.3 lb/100 gal or	16.6 gm/mile (bus)

Estimates of the typical loading factors are 1.2 to 1.5 passengers per automobile, 68 per Boeing 707 jet (capacity 130), 20 in an average streetcar (capacity 140), and about half capacity for a train or a bus (capacities 1400 and 50, respectively).

Of course, such a system needs public support to operate economically.

The relative costs

What are the relative costs of public mass transit versus the private automobile? Taking a total view, it is clear that any system that uses less capital equipment to move more people at greater operating efficiency must be less expensive. From a personal point of view the greater economy of mass transit may not be apparent, but think about it.

You subsidize public transit with your fares and, to a certain extent, with your taxes. You pay for automobile expenses too. You invest a large sum to buy the car and an additional sum to maintain it. You pay a lot to insure it—more if you pay commuter rates. Operating expenses alone are likely to be a minimum of 2 to 3¢ per mile, but the 7¢ per mile and up that car rental agencies charge better reflects the total cost.

In addition, there are the hidden costs of the taxes spent for increasing the capacity of the road system and for the storm sewer systems that must handle the extra water runoff, and of the taxes not collected because untaxable roads have displaced tax–producing urban property. There is also the added burden of pollution from greater emissions and from more fuel extraction and transport.

Intercity

As in the city, you have the option to take either your car or mass transportation when you travel between cities. For the subway and the streetcar substitute the train and add the airplane. The fact remains that the automobile is still a relatively inefficient and expensive way to move people. Rail transportation and buses are much to be preferred.

Over long distances, speed becomes important. There the fast pace of modern living tends to demand air travel, despite its greater price. Unless something can be done about our frantic life style, air travel is unlikely to lose much of its business to less environmentally harmful modes of transportation.

The medium haul is the area where we can and should be doing better. Here, the railroad is the obvious choice. It combines speed with low fuel consumption per passenger mile and has low emissions (See Table 35). The Japanese and Europeans have demonstrated what can be done to create fast and efficient rail service, and Americans have shown that they will ride trains, if they are offered decent service. In 1969, two hundred thousand of them used rail travel to see Europe, and back in their own country many more have kept the Metroliner between New York and Washington and the Turbotrain to Boston well-patronized though they operate at far less than their designed speeds.

The Metroliner is a step in the proper direction. How about the other transportation innovations recently introduced and on the drawing boards? Air shuttles and helicopter taxis have met with considerable success, but in the broad view they must be seen as devices for circumventing the failure of ground systems that can do the same jobs more efficiently and less obnoxiously. A full helicopter uses about 26 times as much fuel per passenger mile as a full train. And nobody wants to live near an airport.

On the long–distance end, the movement seems to be toward larger and faster planes. The 747 is an advance; it moves more people with greater efficiency and less noise. On the other hand, the SST would move fewer people with lower efficiency and much greater noise. To save a few businessmen a couple of hours, literally millions will be exposed to the sonic boom each time the plane flies. The effects on climate are not known, but they are potentially catastrophic.

Toward a better future

To summarize, you face a series of choices. Each time you make one, you have a chance to act for or against your own long–range good and that of your society. There are things you can do today that may be as minor as buying a tank of unleaded gasoline or taking a bus when normally you would have used your car. Buy a bicycle; walk more. Each act contributes. Get in the habit and encourage others to do the same and the impact will be significant. When a major decision does arise, apply the same criteria. Be willing to try something new. If you have always taken a plane, try the train. If you have always bought large cars, try a compact economy model. When vacation time comes, explore areas near home instead of making the grand trek.

It will sometimes take patience and a willingness to put up with some inconvenience. This is part of the new life style. It is part of the conversion process. A degree of equanimity will enable you to survive the inevitable inconveniences that come even when you use the "more convenient" modes of getting around. At the same time you should channel your inevitable frustration into constructive actions. Let the transportation managers know when their system hasn't worked as it should.

When significant numbers of people begin to act in this way, the impact will be felt. Not everyone has to stop using a product or service to make it economically unfeasible. Conversely, a small but significant increase in patronage can greatly benefit something good.

The pages that follow present information that hopefully will be beneficial to your getting from here to there— that is, to your moving away from high–cost, polluting transport to more-efficient methods that preserve a livable world.

THE CAR

Gasolines

Judging by their advertising campaigns, the large oil companies who sell you gasoline have been doing a lot to halt air pollution. By buying this or that gasoline with special additive X, Y, and/or Z you are told that hydrocarbons and carbon monoxide can be cut by so many percent. They attach plastic balloons to the tail pipes so that you can actually *see* the wonderful effects of using their gasoline and they marshal all sorts of "test results" and expert opinion to back up their claims. The fact is that the miraculous results trumpeted to the skies by the advertising staffs of the oil companies will never clean up those skies. The *main* problem is not with the gasoline. But read on.

The gasoline that is burned in your car's engine is a mixture of a hundred or more chemical compounds, most of them hydrocarbons that give off heat energy when they combine with oxygen. The various components of the hydrocarbon mixture contribute different properties to the gasoline. In particular, some components cause the mixture to burn more evenly, without "knock." The octane rating of a gasoline is a measure of how it compares with a set of standard hydrocarbon mixtures (iso–octane mixed with heptane) in terms of knock. The higher the octane rating, the greater the resistance to knocking.

High–compression cars require higher octane gasoline (in the neighborhood of 98 octane) while lower performance engines should be run with lower octane gas (around 94). A VW gets along perfectly well with 91 octane gas.

Lead in fuel. Something like six additives are commonly mixed into gasolines as part of the refining process. They are added to prevent aging of the fuel, to prevent rust and icing, to assist starting in cold weather, to prevent formation of deposits, and to boost the octane of the gasoline. Tetraethyl lead (TEL), probably the best-known additive, is used because it has the effect of increasing octane ratings without costing much (in dollars). The alternative to lead is to blend in higher octane hydrocarbons, but they are somewhat more expensive to make.

Currently, regular gasolines contain about 2.5 grams of lead per gallon of gas, while the premium grades contain an average of about 2.8 grams (some as high as 4 grams per gallon). This adds up to an annual use of 265,000 tons of lead—20% of the total U.S. consumption. In addition, 85% of the sodium metal used in this country goes to making the organoleads, and about three fourths of the bromine production goes to making ethylene dibromide, 90% of which is used as a scavenger to prevent lead deposits in car engines.

A quarter to a half of the lead ends up in the air as particulates, the part of air pollution that you can see. Eventually it settles to the ground around our highways. Enough reaches your lungs and your stomach by way of food so that the average American now carries about one hundred times the concentration of lead that was common before TEL was introduced. The full effect that this is having on human health is uncertain, in part because the research in this field has for many years been dominated by researchers in the employ of the lead additive manufacturers. A National Air Pollution Control Administration study has reportedly found a correlation between lead dustfall in residential areas and cardiovascular disease. Lead poisoning from eating peeling lead–based paint is known to have killed ghetto children, and some people believe lead poisoning did in Roman civilization (the Romans ate from lead vessels). It is surely safe to say lead from auto exhaust doesn't do you much good.

After a good bit of jockeying around among the auto companies, oil, and the government, it appears that most maufacturers will design their 1971 cars to operate on non–leaded fuel and that the gasoline companies will have low–lead regular octane gasolines on the market by fall 1970. Low–lead gasoline (0.5 grams per gallon) will probable be introduced during the transition. Thus, the buyer will have a choice.

Buy non–leaded gasoline if it is available. Amoco has marketed a no–lead premium (high octane) gas for some time. Non–leaded fuel for cars designed for lower octane fuel should be available shortly. Ask for it. You may have to pay more per gallon (an equalizing tax on lead may make up the difference), but you should recover some of the extra cost because of reduced wear on spark plugs, tailpipe, and muffler. (The ethylene bromide scavenger that comes along with the lead is corrosive).

The debate over how much the switch to non–leaded fuels is actually going to cost has been interesting. As one would expect, the high estimates, 3½ to 4¢ per gallon, have come from Ethyl Corporation, maker of TEL, and the lowest one from Universal Oil Products, maker of a catalytic muffler that requires unleaded gas. The latter estimates the switch can be made for 1¢ or less per gallon.

Detergent additives. Standard Oil of California, Mobil, and other oil companies have tried to capitalize on the recent interest in air pollution. In enormously expensive ad campaigns they have proudly announced their detergent additives, which are supposed to keep the PCV valves clean and thereby reduce emissions. The positive crankcase ventilation (PCV) system was introduced nationwide in the mid–1960s to cut out the 25% of hydrocarbon emissions that came from the crankcase vent. (A PCV system recycles the acidic blowby gases. These cause the crankcase oil to sludge; thus, the detergents.)

Standard Oil's F–310, however, "the most outstanding development in automotive fuel technology in years," has, in the opinion of many, been little more than an advertising hoax. California Air Resources Board tests have indicated that cars in a normal state of maintenance showed no significant changes in the emission of pollutants when switched to F–310. Apparently the cars that Standard sent to Scott Research Laboratories for inspection and testing had been specially gummed up. The 42% and 67% reduction figures were very misleading. In fact, Union Oil now claims that Scott tests have proven that F–310 is no better than the gasoline they market, and a bill in the Hawaiian (Chevron Island?) legislature would establish a full–time investigation aimed at indicting Standard for fraudulent advertising.

The Chevron claims are useful in illustrating how difficult it can be to evaluate advertising information. A claim of a 50% reduction is meaningless unless you know what the numbers mean—50% from what or to what? For example, the Scott tests were run on cars that were emitting six and seven hundred p.p.m. hydrocarbons. This is far above what most cars emit, 225 p.p.m. being normal for a new car and about 300 p.p.m. for models from 1966 on after 32,000 miles or more. The average motorist with a normally clean engine could thus never even begin to realize Standard's deceptively inflated claims.

Emissions

The air pollutants from your car that are most harmful are not visible. Furthermore, the visible part of the exhaust is only a small fraction of the total emitted by your car unless it is way out of adjustment. By mass, carbon monoxide is the major pollutant.

Standards. Because of the horrendous smog conditions that have existed in the Los Angeles basin for a long time, California has led the nation in setting automobile emissions standards. Until recently, California's have been several years ahead of national standards.

Emission levels have commonly been measured in terms of the ratio of pollutant to air in the exhaust, either in parts per million (ppm) or in percent. The problem with this practice has been that two cars, one belching out large quantities of pollutants and another emitting few, would have the same pollution concentration as long as the big polluter also spewed out more air. Now emissions standards are expressed in the more readily understandable units of grams of pollutant per mile. To compare the old levels with the new, or for that matter the old with the old, one needs to know the displacement of the engines and other factors.

Table 36 presents emissions standards set by California and by the U.S. government, levels established as goals, typical levels, and emissions levels of several alternatives to the gasoline-powered internal-combustion engine.

As can be seen from the table, emissions control has had an effect on emissions levels. Compare pre-1966 with 1969. It is also clear that putting mileage on a car reduces performance (increases pollution). The emissions standards are supposed to apply to a car as long as it is on the road; however, there is ample evidence to indicate that many cars exceed the standards even before they leave the factory. Under present regulations, auto manufacturers are allowed to submit four regularly equipped

TABLE 36. AUTOMOBILE EMISSIONS
(All figures in grams per mile)

STANDARDS	Hydro Carbons	Carbon Monoxide	Oxides of Nitrogen
California 1966	3.4	34.0	—
California 1971	2.2	23.0	4.0
California 1972	1.5	23.0	3.0
California 1974	1.5	23.0	1.3
Federal 1968	3.3	34.0	—
Federal 1970	2.2	23.0	—
Federal 1973	2.2	23.0	3.0
Federal 1975[1]	0.5	11.0	0.9
GOALS			
California Goals	0.5	11.0	0.75
[2]Morse Report Goals for '75	0.6	12.0	1.0
[3]IEEC Goals	0.82	7.1	0.68
TYPICAL EMISSIONS			
Pre-1966 cars	11	80	4
1969 Cars @ 4,000 miles	3.0	20	
Cars @ 50,000 miles	3.7	25	
MODIFIED CONVENTIONAL ENGINES			
Sun Oil test vehicle	0.7	12.0	0.6
Chrysler-Esso engines			
Manifold reactor	1.5	20.0	1.3
Catalytic reactor	1.7	12.0	1.0
Synchrothermal reactor	0.25	7.0	0.6
Ethyl Corp. "lean reactor"	0.7	10.4	2.5
DuPont manifold reactor	0.22	7.4	0.41
ALTERNATIVE POWER PLANTS AND FUELS			
Steam car	0.2-0.7	1.0-4.0	0.15-0.4
Gas turbine	0.5-1.2	3.0-7.0	1.3-5.2
Wankel engine	1.8	23.0	2.2
Stirling hybrid	0.006	0.3	2.2
Natural gas fuel	1.5	6.0	1.5

[1]In addition, a Federal limit of 0.1 grams/mile on particulate emissions is to be established in 1975. Current uncontrolled levels are about 0.3 grams/mile.

Notes: California standards are set in the Pure Air Act; goals in the Low Emission Vehicle Act.
[2]Morse Report—a 1967 U.S. Department of Commerce report. *"The Automobile and Air Pollution."*
[3]IEEC—Inter–Industry Emission Control (Ford-Mobil)

Source: The table is largely from *Environmental Science & Techology,* April 1970.

For comparison, the 1968 Federal emissions standards using the concentration scale are presented below:

TABLE 37. 1968 FEDERAL EMISSIONS STANDARDS

Engine Displacement	Hydrocarbons	Carbon Dioxide
50 to 100 cu. in.	410 ppm.	2.3%
100 to 140 cu. in.	350 ppm.	2.0%
More than 140 cu. in.	275 ppm.	1.5%

but hand–tuned and specially selected cars to be tested by the Federal Air Pollution Control Administration (FAPCA). These four cars are supposed to represent as many as a million or more assembly–line vehicles of the same model. If the prototypes fail the first time they can be tinkered with and sent back to try again and again. Thus, there should be little wonder that the car you buy probably doesn't meet the standards. Table 38 presents some test data on road vehicles used by car rental agencies. Mileage on the cars ranged as high as 22,000 and averaged 10,000.

TABLE 38. FAILURE OF CARS TO MEET FEDERAL
STANDARDS

Company	Engine Size (c.i.d.)	Number Tested	% Failing Hydro-Carbons	% Failing Carbon Monoxide
American Motors	290	32	0%	13%
General Motors	307	44	64%	50%
Chevrolet Division	327 ('68)	48	42%	58%
	327 ('69)	52	10%	46%
Chrysler	225	18	6%	39%
	318	49	12%	10%
Ford	289	45	62%	22%
	302	110	58%	19%
	390	116	16%	16%
General Motors	350	25	16%	56%
Pontiac Division	400	23	0%	48%
Volkswagen	91.1	31	32%	16%

Source: The table is an abridgement of one in the April 1970 issue of *Environmental Science & Technology*, whose ultimate source was the National Air Pollution Control Administration.

The message of the figures presented in table 38 is not "don't bother trying to buy a car with low pollution emissions." Rather the message is "don't expect to get what you should be getting."

Actually, even if your car meets the test standards, it may not perform as cleanly in regular driving conditions. In the test procedure, cars are run through a seven–mode, seven–cycle program that is supposed to simulate standard driving conditions in Los Angeles. The conditions in

New York are not the same. Also, some tests are from a cold start, while in others the cars are warmed up first.

A car owner who wants to check his car against the standards should first consult his dealer. In some states the air pollution control agency may have the proper equipment and be more reliable. In California, check with the Air Resources Control Board.

A car buyer who wants to know how much his prospective purchase will pollute should ask the seller. The information should be made available. In Massachusetts, a bill has been introduced that would require every motor vehicle displayed for sale to bear a label containing the levels of pollutants the vehicle will emit and the following warning—"Caution: the exhaust emissions of this product are pollutants hazardous to your health and to the health of others."

Emissions control devices. Cars sold after the implementation of the California and national emissions standards are equipped with devices designed to meet the standards that were in effect at the time the car was made. Older cars lack such devices unless a conversion kit has been installed.

The devices installed in 1968 and 1969 cars cost buyers an estimated $18 per car; in 1970, $36 per car for the stricter standards; and in 1971, estimates add $12 more. Compared to the cost of a car and the cost of air pollution, this is an incredible bargain.

The effects of the new devices will not be seen immediately because of the large number of old cars still on the road without any emissions control system. If you own such a car you don't need to trade it in to make your contribution to cleaner air. Investigate one of the conversion kits that are becoming available to clean up old cars' "bad breath". GM, Ford, and Chrysler have announced devices that are supposed to bring pre–1966 cars up to about 1969 standards. Costs are in the $10 range, plus an hour's labor for installation and adjustment of timing and carburetor.

Shopping for an emissions control system is not unlike looking at high–fidelity systems. You look at the

TABLE 39. UNION OIL PERFORMANCE TESTS—
COMPARATIVE FUEL ECONOMY OF AMERICAN CARS

	ENGINE SPECIFICATIONS					FUEL ECONOMY
	LENGTH IN.	CURB WEIGHT LBS.	ENGINE TYPE	HORSEPOWER	CUBIC INCHES	MILES PER GALLON

CLASS 1 SUPER DELUXE (2 DOOR HARDTOP)

	LENGTH IN.	CURB WEIGHT LBS.	ENGINE TYPE	HORSEPOWER	CUBIC INCHES	MILES PER GALLON
Buick Electra 225 Custom	225.8	4567	V-8	370	455	15.179
Buick Riviera	215.5	4427	V-8	370	455	15.722
Chrysler New Yorker	224.7	4486	V-8	350	440	14.581
Oldsmobile 98	225.2	4475	V-8	365	455	15.010
Oldsmobile Toronado	214.3	4638	V-8	375	455	13.388
Thunderbird	212.5	4573	V-8	360	429	14.823

All models will have power steering, power brakes, and air conditioning.

CLASS 2 DELUXE 8 CYLINDER (4 DOOR SEDAN OR HARDTOP)

	LENGTH IN.	CURB WEIGHT LBS.	ENGINE TYPE	HORSEPOWER	CUBIC INCHES	MILES PER GALLON
Buick Wildcat Custom	220.2	4392	V-8	370	455	15.808
Chrysler 300	224.7	4548	V-8	350	440	15.416
Dodge Monaco	220.4	4375	V-8	350	440	14.753
Mercury Marquis	224.3	4379	V-8	360	429	13.997
Oldsmobile Delta 88 Custom	219.1	4362	V-8	365	455	15.105
Pontiac Bonneville	224.6	4519	V-8	360	455	15.811

All models will have power steering, power brakes, and air conditioning.

CLASS 3 MEDIUM 8 CYLINDER (2 DOOR OR 4 DOOR SEDAN OR HARDTOP)

	LENGTH IN.	CURB WEIGHT LBS.	ENGINE TYPE	HORSEPOWER	CUBIC INCHES	MILES PER GALLON
Buick LeSabre Custom	220.2	4116	V-8	260	350	15.851
Chevrolet Caprice	216.0	4039	V-8	250	350	16.627
Chrysler Newport Custom	224.7	4297	V-8	290	383	16.114
*Dodge Polara Custom	220.4	4216	V-8	290	383	16.134
Ford LTD	216.0	4139	V-8	250	351	16.096
Mercury Monterey	221.8	4270	V-8	265	390	15.102
Oldsmobile Delta 88	219.1	4204	V-8	250	350	15.073
Plymouth Sport Fury	214.9	3956	V-8	230	318	16.517
Pontiac Executive	223.9	4345	V-8	290	400	16.619

All models will have power steering, power brakes, and air conditioning.

*.3MPG penalty—Driver Error.

	LENGTH IN.	CURB WEIGHT LBS.	ENGINE TYPE	HORSEPOWER	CUBIC INCHES	MILES PER GALLON
	ENGINE SPECIFICATIONS				FUEL ECONOMY	

CLASS 4 STANDARD 8 CYLINDER (4 DOOR SEDAN OR HARDTOP)

	LENGTH IN.	CURB WEIGHT LBS.	ENGINE TYPE	HORSEPOWER	CUBIC INCHES	MILES PER GALLON
Ambassador DPL	208.0	3655	V-8	210	304	16.717
Chevrolet Bel Air	216.0	3943	V-8	250	350	17.819
Dodge Polara	220.4	4101	V-8	230	318	15.652
Ford Custom 500	213.9	3906	V-8	220	302	17.182
Plymouth Fury II	214.9	3911	V-8	230	318	17.670
Pontiac Catalina	217.9	4326	V-8	255	350	14.930

All cars will have power steering, power brakes, and air conditioning.

CLASS 5 INTERMEDIATE 8 CYLINDER (4 DOOR SEDAN OR HARDTOP)

	LENGTH IN.	CURB WEIGHT LBS.	ENGINE TYPE	HORSEPOWER	CUBIC INCHES	MILES PER GALLON
Buick Skylark Custom	206.2	3718	V-8	260	350	16.853
Chevelle Malibu	201.2	3475	V-8	200	307	17.348
Dodge Coronet 500	209.7	3461	V-8	230	318	17.349
Ford Torino	206.2	3403	V-8	220	302	18.082
Mercury Montego MX	209.9	3419	V-8	220	302	18.165
Olds Cutlass	207.2	3653	V-8	250	350	15.870
Plymouth Sport Satellite	203.8	3375	V-8	230	318	17.511
Pontiac LeMans	206.5	3393	V-8	255	350	16.435
Rebel SST	199.0	3429	V-8	210	304	16.597

All cars will have power steering.

	LENGTH IN.	CURB WEIGHT LBS.	ENGINE TYPE	HORSEPOWER	CUBIC INCHES	MILES PER GALLON
		ENGINE SPECIFICATIONS			FUEL ECONOMY	

CLASS 6 COMPACT 6 CYLINDER (2 DOOR SEDAN OR HARDTOP)

	LENGTH IN.	CURB WEIGHT LBS.	ENGINE TYPE	HORSEPOWER	CUBIC INCHES	MILES PER GALLON
AMC Hornet SST	179.3	2787	6	145	232	25.075
Chevy Nova 6	189.4	2963	6	140	230	20.531
Dodge Dart Swinger	196.2	2972	6	145	225	22.487
Ford Maverick	179.4	2532	6	120	200	22.153
Plymouth Valiant Duster	188.4	2939	6	145	225	22.190

CLASS 7 SPORT INTERMEDIATE (2 DOORS)

	LENGTH IN.	CURB WEIGHT LBS.	ENGINE TYPE	HORSEPOWER	CUBIC INCHES	MILES PER GALLON
Buick GS 455	202.2	3746	V-8	350	455	16.325
Dodge Charger R/T	208.5	3816	V-8	375	440	13.279
Ford Torino Cobra	206.2	3919	V-8	370	429	14.059
Merc Cyclone GT	209.9	3933	V-8	370	429	#
Oldsmobile 442	203.2	3762	V-8	365	455	15.571
Plymouth GTX	203.8	3732	V-8	375	440	14.417
Pontiac GTO	202.9	3776	V-8	360	455	15.913

All cars will have power steering and power brakes.

#Car withdrawn—faulty valve train.

CLASS 8 SUPER SPORT COMPACT (2 DOORS)

	LENGTH IN.	CURB WEIGHT LBS.	ENGINE TYPE	HORSEPOWER	CUBIC INCHES	MILES PER GALLON
Chevy Nova SS	189.4	3349	V-8	300	350	17.503
Dodge Challenger 340	191.3	3512	V-8	275	340	16.208
Javelin SST	191.0	3276	V-8	290	360	17.302
Mercury Cougar XR-7	196.1	3499	V-8	300	351	16.978
Mustang Mach 1	187.4	3416	V-8	300	351	16.952
Plymouth Cuda	186.7	3500	V-8	275	340	16.260

All cars will have power steering and power brakes.

CLASS 9 SPORT COMPACT (2 DOORS)

	LENGTH IN.	CURB WEIGHT LBS.	ENGINE TYPE	HORSEPOWER	CUBIC INCHES	MILES PER GALLON
Chevy Nova 8	189.4	3201	V-8	200	307	19.492
Dodge Challenger	191.3	3242	V-8	230	318	16.997
Javelin	191.0	3200	V-8	210	304	16.681
*Mercury Cougar	196.1	3414	V-8	250	351	17.233
Mustang	187.4	3159	V-8	220	302	18.335
Plymouth Barracuda	186.7	3186	V-8	230	318	17.565

All cars will have power steering.

*.3MPG penalty—Driver Error.

specifications and puzzle over the complex–sounding technology. To simplify, there are basically two types of emissions control systems. The first tries to stop formation of the pollutants in the engine; the second tries to do something about the pollutants once they have gotten into the exhaust system. In the first approach, conditions in the cylinder are adjusted to favor complete oxidation of the hydrocarbons in the fuel by making the fuel–air mixture richer in air (therefore in oxygen) and by keeping the combustion temperature high. This system does reduce hydrocarbon and carbon monoxide emissions, but it has the unfortunate effect of promoting the oxidation of nitrogen as well. Cars that have been designed in this way to meet only the hydrocarbon and carbon monoxide standards throw more nitrogen oxides into the atmosphere. California has actually seen an increase in NO_x emissions. Although systems that would remove NO_x by reacting it with CO in the presence of a catalyst (divided catalyst bed systems) have been conceived, other approaches apparently offer more promise.

Another common system, illustrative of the second approach, tries to get rid of the pollutants as they come through the exhaust. In an exhaust manifold thermal reactor, exhaust gases and air are mixed at high temperatures. Again the hydrocarbons and CO are oxidized, and so is nitrogen. This type of system is commonly installed in cars with manual transmissions.

The newer systems aimed at reducing NO_x as well as hydrocarbons (HC) and CO approach the problem by reducing the combustion temperature in the engine and sometimes by increasing the fuel–to–air ratio. This produces more HC and CO, but reduces NO_x, and the HC and CO can be dealt with in a catalytic reactor. Any system using this approach will have the disadvantage of using slightly more fuel because lowering the combustion temperature thermodynamically decreases the efficiency. The new cars designed to reduce NO_x thus sacrifice a small degree of "performance" to reduce pollution. The Esso "synchrothermal" system is illustrative of what this sort of a system can achieve.

The catalytic reactor achieves the further oxidation of the CO and HC without resorting to the high temperatures of the manifold thermal reactors. The problem with the catalytic reactors is that the catalysts tend to be rather expensive. The catalysts also tend to be poisoned by the lead additives. Actually it is the imminent advent of the catalytic exhaust control systems, not the threat that lead poses to human health, that caused the recent movement to ban lead in gasoline. The public has been treated to the unlikely spectacle of automobile and lead–additive manufacturers actually instituting crash research programs to achieve emissions control. DuPont and Ethyl Corporation, makers of tetraethyl lead, are understandably eager to demonstrate the feasibility of systems that will operate with leaded gas. Recent tests of the DuPont thermal exhaust manifold system indicate that it can deliver low emissions even with leaded gas. Estimates of cost to the consumer for this system and the catalytic reactors, however, are in the $150 to $300 range, according to the auto industry.

Because of the essentially monopolistic control that the automobile and gasoline industries have over the servicing of cars, the consumer's choice of emissions control systems will probably be limited to the ones those industries decide to introduce. It is difficult for outsiders to break into the market. Ask your auto dealer, service garage, or auto parts stores for the particulars on auto pollution control systems.

A Further Note. Actually there are three types of emissions from automobiles. Crankcase emissions and exhaust emissions have been discussed, but evaporation from the carburetor and fuel system has not been mentioned. This sort of emission has accounted for about 15% of the total hydrocarbons emitted. The 1970 California standards and the 1971 federal standards set limits for evaporation. Present control systems store fuel vapors in the crankcase or in charcoal cannisters, but this is less than adequate. The problem may eventually require a change in the properties of gasoline.

Alternative fuels

Switching to natural gas fuel is a well-tested alternative that is available today. The internal combustion engine can be powered by compressed natural gas (CNG), liquid natural gas (LNG), or by liquid propane gas (LPG). Each system has its drawbacks and its advantages. On the positive side, all three systems cut down emissions substantially. Tests on operating vehicles have indicated typical emissions are:

<u>CNG</u>

2.1 gms./mile HC
7.5 gms./mile CO
1.9 gms./mile NO_x

<u>LPG</u>

0.88 gms./mile HC
4.1 gms./mile CO
1.9 gms./mile NO_x

Additionally, the effects of the hydrocarbon emissions are less harmful because the hydrocarbons emitted are less reactive in forming smog than those from gasoline; with natural gas the reactivity factor is ½, with propane, about ¾.

Also, operating and maintenance costs are drastically cut. Based on the BTU content of the fuel, natural gas- and propane-powered vehicles make more efficient use of the fuel. Natural gas fuels are generally cheaper than gasoline; however, most of the difference in price is caused by the taxes that are imposed on gasoline but not on natural gas—yet. Engine life is doubled; sparkplugs last 50,000 miles; and oil changes are needed only once a year.

On the negative side, the main problem is the availability of fuel—there is no vast network of natural gas stations. At present, there are only 14 natural gas liquefaction plants in the country, and LNG must be stored at −258°F, which means that a network of small LNG stations is not very feasible. On the other hand, most towns of 50,000 or more have propane gas dealers. The biggest disadvantage of CNG is traveling range. One gas cylinder carries only enough fuel to go 40 to 50 miles. As a result, most CNG systems are equipped with a dual fuel system and a choke–like button that permits the user to select natural gas in the city and gasoline out in the open. LNG and LPG have ranges comparable to gasoline.

The fuel availability problems and limited range are easily overcome by fleet operators (Taxi companies and delivery systems); CNG, LNG, and LPG are all used in fleet operation. In fact, about 250,000 vehicles are using LPG in the United States today. In Japan, 200,000 automobiles run on LPG.

Another problem arises from the fact that cars have not been designed for conversion to natural gas systems. Unless space isn't a problem (as in a pick–up truck), the extra cylinders and tanks can be pretty bulky.

The cost of conversion is about $300 for CNG and LPG, and the job can be done quite easily in less than a day. Local propane dealers often do conversions to LPG. Check under "gas" in *The Yellow Pages*. In some cases extended payment arrangements can be made. The LNG conversion is substantially more expensive. Half of the $800 cost goes for the special insulated tank that is required.

With LPG there is also a safety factor. Because propane gas is denser than air, a leak could cause it to collect in an explosive mixture. For this reason LPG is not allowed in the tunnels that lead into Manhattan. Experience has shown, however, that liquid propane is, at present, a reasonable low–polluting alternative to gasoline.

At present the oil companies are all geared to produce gasoline. At current prices, they say, it is not profitable for them to explore for more natural gas, and so, in the last year, natural gas has actually been used at a faster rate than new reserves have been discovered. Given this situation, converting all automobiles to natural gas, which would increase demand by one third, might not be a viable alternative.

A rise in the price of gas or the possibility of producing gas from coal could quickly change the supply picture. In addition, a large quantity of natural gas now generated in coal mines is wasted by discharge into the atmosphere, where it becomes a pollutant.

The decomposition of garbage, manure, or sewage under the proper anaerobic conditions also produces natural gas (methane). Proposals have been made to light nighttime golf games on courses built atop old dumps with the gas that is generated underground. In other cases, farmers out in the boondocks have been able to generate power from decomposing manure. Chicken droppings work well. Several cars are actually run with a chicken, not a tiger, in the tank.

Diesel engines

The diesel engine is widely used, especially on trucks and buses. Believe it or not, a properly working diesel actually pollutes less in some respects than your car engine. Because the diesel burns hotter, combustion is more complete. This reduces hydrocarbons and carbon monoxide to low levels but tends to increase nitrogen oxides. New kits are available to reduce emissions and noise from bus diesels, but for the automobile, the diesel is not much of an improvement over the gasoline–powered i.c.e.

Wankel engines

The Wankel engine is a rotary internal combustion engine that has the advantage over the standard reciprocating–piston type of being smaller and more compact. Commercial production of cars with this engine has already taken place in Japan (Toyo Kogyo Co.) and in Germany (NSU Co.). NSU has produced 10,000 units of its Ro–80 full–scale sedans.

The Wankel engine, however, is at least as polluting as the normal i.c.e., but with exhaust reactor systems it too can be brought up to currently acceptable levels.

Away from internal combustion

Of the 4200 vehicles manufactured in 1900, 1680 of them were steam–powered, 1580 electric, and only 940 were gasoline–powered. Obviously times have changed.

The internal combustion engine (i.c.e.) won out not because the alternative power plants were wholly uncompetitive. The perceived advantages that led to the investment of larger amounts in i.c.e. research were relatively small. Since that time infinitely more research has gone into the perfection of the i.c.e. than into steam, electric, or other power alternatives. But today, faced with the new challenges posed by air pollution, we find manufacturers patching up the old power plants. Automobiles have become such complex machines that it is no wonder that they don't work the way one would have them work. It is time for a fresh look.

A large number of working prototypes of other systems have been built. Many of them have significant advantages over the internal combustion engine—both in terms of emissions, and in economy of operation and maintenance. At the present time, however, none of them has been mass–produced, and only when the economies of mass production come into play will they provide a feasible alternative for the general car buyer.

Unfortunately, the gasoline–powered internal combustion engine is today so entrenched that switching to another power system would require an enormous adjustment. The magnitude of the adjustment is underscored by the fact that of the twenty largest companies in the United States, at least twelve would be involved in such a switch in a major way. The difficulty of the switch, however, has been greatly overstated. Standard Oil, Mobil, Texaco, Gulf, Shell, and the others will still have a market because they sell energy. G.M., Ford, and Chrysler will probably still manufacture the vehicles regardless of how they are powered.

The biggest obstacles in the way of better power systems for private and public vehicles is the inertia of Detroit. Innovation is coming from outside the industry. With government help and prodding, new systems will become available. At hearings on low–emission vehicles before a joint subcommittee of the Senate Commerce and Public Works Committees, William Lear, who has had experience developing both the steam and gas turbine engines, confidently predicted, "I believe that 15 years from today that an internal combustion car will be an oddity" (January 29, 1970).

Electric cars. Reportedly, New York City's first speeding ticket went to the operator of an electric–powered automobile. Although the electric is no longer common, there are, in England, about 60,000 electric vehicles that are used mostly for short delivery routes. In addition, the U.S. has a population of about 150,000 golf carts that are powered by electric storage batteries.

For certain purposes, the electric–powered vehicle has an impressive list of advantages. Aside from a small amount of ozone, the car produces no air pollution during operation. It operates quietly, a significant asset when one remembers that in cities about 85% of noise is supposed to come from i.c.e. powered vehicles. Although the electric lacks speed and extended range at present, most city and suburban driving requires neither.

The most commonly mentioned problem regarding large–scale use of electric-powered automobiles is the vastly increased load this would put on the electric power industry. While cars would not pollute the air directly, the power plants would. In a study prepared by the National Economic Research Associates, the estimate was made that if all the automotive vehicles operating in the U.S. in 1968 had been electric, their energy demands would have added about 43% to the load on electric utilities. That would mean exchanging a substantial increase in electric power production for the abolishment of automobile air pollution. It is not immediately clear which would be more desirable.

The i.c.e. is only about 15% efficient. Thermodynamically, the highest efficiency possible is 25% to 30%, but this has not been achieved. Part of the reason it hasn't is that the i.c.e. usually operates at far from its optimum; idling is, of course, wholly wasteful. The electric car wouldn't lose energy in this way. Assuming an efficiency of generation of electric power of 35%, and taking into account the losses of energy in the motor (10%), charging the batteries (20%), and transmitting the power

(10%), one can calculate that the overall efficiency of an electric vehicle would be about 23%, based on the energy content of the power–plant fuel. This is a substantial improvement in efficiency over the i.c.e., and would tend to mean less pollution for this reason, though the nature of the pollution would differ.

From an energy–resource point of view, therefore, the electric car might be a good idea. If fuel cells with efficiencies larger than 35% become economically feasible, or if nuclear or fossil–fuel energy can ever be made truly clean, then electrically driven automobiles will become the vehicles of choice.

Coming back to the present, however, one must recognize that fuel cell technology is not ready and that present battery systems are either much heavier than one would want or too expensive. Working within these limits, a number of prototypes of electric cars have been built. In 1967–68 there was a great flurry of interest in electric cars, but to date no widely acceptable model is on the market.

The word "acceptable" is the key. Electric cars do not have the performance of the high-powered i.c.e. monsters of today. But it is not at all clear that any car should. If you are looking for a second car for errands, however, existing electric vehicles should be acceptable. For that matter, so should any small, low–powered vehicle. In fact, the greatest virtue that electric vehicles may have is that they may enable people to think beyond the framework that demands bigness and power.

■ Electric Fuel Propulsion, Inc., of Detroit has delivered 42 of its Mars II electric automobiles, mainly to electric utilities. They are capable of speeds up to 70 mph, can cruise at 40 mph for 150 miles, and can be charged to 80% of capacity in 45 minutes. A similar vehicle was demonstrated in New York in December 1969. It can be mass–produced at between $3500 and $4000 and costs only $1.20 for a full charge.

■ British Ford has a prototype electric called the Commuta which will move two adults and two children 40 miles at 25 mph. In a *Playboy* article (May 1970) it is described as "pretty well ready for the market, should there be a market."

■ "Enfield Automotive of England some time ago announced firm production plans for a four–seater electric pointed toward the U.S. market and selling at around $1000; so far this vehicle has not appeared on the market. The Enfield has a top speed of 40 mph, a 35–mile range, [and] an eight-hour recharge period," according to *Playboy*.

■ Cushman Motors of Lincoln, Nebraska, is the largest producer of electric golfcarts. It also produces a line of vehicles that sell from $750 to $1490 whose primary use is in industrial plants.

■ Stelber Industries of Elmhurst, New York, has an electrically assisted "electric cycle" that, on electric power, has a range of sixty miles at 15 mph.

Rankine engines. Rankine engines are external combustion engines that use a working fluid in a closed system to deliver energy that drives a piston or turbine. The working fluid may be steam as in the steam car, hydrogen or helium as in the Sterling engine, or another fluid. In testimony taken before the Senate Committee on Commerce the following advantages of Rankine engines over the internal combustion engine were enumerated:

> "The Rankine vehicle is more economical to operate because it gets better gasoline mileage using less expensive fuels, and because it has better maintenance and reliability potential. Its acceleration, auxiliary operation, and braking characteristics are superior to those of the ICE. Alleged 'problems' in applying Rankine cycle systems to automotive use have been or are being solved. The Rankine cycle engine is as safe as the ICE; it consumes no more water; freeze-up can be avoided; and startup time is satisfactory. In terms of the all–important exhaust emission characteristics, the Rankine cycle system is far superior to the ICE."

To elaborate slightly, startup time is 20 seconds with a cold engine. Kerosene, low–octane gasoline, natural gas, oil, and even coal can be used to power a Rankine engine. Antiques with 600,000 miles on the odometer are still going strong.

Working models of steam- and other Rankine–engine–powered cars have been around for some time. The Williams brothers of Ambler, Pa., have years of experience building steam–powered vehicles. In 1969, with the entry of William Lear into the field, it looked like the steam car was really on its way. Then late in 1969 it was announced that Lear had abandoned the steam automobile as unworkable.

The fact of the matter is that Lear is continuing his steam work but has decided that the ultimate automotive power plant is the gas turbine and that, "I didn't think the industry could tolerate two major changes in propulsion systems." Lear testified in January 1970 before joint subcommittee hearings in the Senate that, ". . . it seems to me that the automotive industry is totally committed to the status quo. They don't want a new engine if they can avoid it. . . . They can only be induced to do it by competition." In his scenario of how this will happen, one of the auto manufacturers, presumably American Motors, which has less of a stake in the status quo, will introduce a car with a new power plant and the other will have to follow.

Gas turbines. The reason Lear has come to favor the gas turbine over steam is primarily because it is mechanically simpler. Like the Rankine–powered car, the gas turbine has very low emissions, it burns readily available inexpensive fuel, and it has been proven in performance and consumer acceptance. In the early 1960s Chrysler built 50 turbine cars which tested out quite successfully.

The main problem seems to be the cost of building the turbines and the rate at which they can be turned out. These are problems that should be solved fairly quickly with a little development money. Turbine engines for trucks and buses are scheduled for introduction in mid-1971 (GM and Ford will be selling them). Thus, the prospects for turbines in automobiles are probably good.

Hybrid vehicles. The car you drive is actually a hybrid, to the extent that it has a battery that starts the engine. It was the introduction of the self–starter that gave the old, hand–cranked i.c.e. the critical advantage over the steam automobile.

More complete hybridization of the automobile has gained a lot of attention recently because it offers a way to overcome the disadvantages of some of the commonly mentioned alternatives to the present i.c.e. For instance, a battery–powered vehicle equipped with an i.c.e. or an e.c.e. power plant that keeps the batteries charged could overcome the range limitation that is imposed by the limited energy density of batteries. In such a system the engine can be operated at a constant output that is near its highest efficiency and lowest emissions' point. The Sterling hybrid is such a car.

Your next car

If we are to believe the experts, the external combustion engine (Rankine or gas turbine) offers the best choice for meeting the emissions standards that we will need later in this decade and in the 1980s. Emissions will have to be lowered beyond the 1975 standards to keep the smog levels from creeping right back up as the number of cars increases. Tacking more abatement devices onto the internal combustion engine doesn't make sense.

In his testimony before the Senate, Lear made the additional point that we haven't really met the transportation problem head on until we confront "the ridiculousness of a 185–pound man driving 20 miles to work in a 5,000 pound automobile." In his estimation "a light–weight car with a 100–horsepower engine would be the maximum that would be required under any circumstances unless you want to get into the LeMans race."

When you buy a car, look at what you are buying— not on the advertiser's terms but on your own terms. Until the car ceases to be a status symbol, tied up with the owner's concept of his sexual adequacy (a connection

---

TRUE HORSEPOWER

GM has announced that it will publish two horse-power ratings for the engines in its 1971 models (Boston *Globe*, July 17, 1970). The gross horse-power, which has been advertised, is obtained from a stripped auto with only essential engine accessories, operating under optimal tuning and atmospheric conditions. The other rating will be lower because it will reflect the actual power available with normal accessory loads and under standard tuning and atmospheric conditions.

While it is refreshing to see the automobile manu-facturers ease up on the bigness–is–better bag, the buyer should understand that the lower horsepower number (for the same engine) does not mean the car is any less overpowered. A 400–horsepower monster simply becomes a 250 "actual" horsepower monster.

---

carefully nurtured by automobile manufacturers' advertis-ing), people will continue to buy much more car than they need or want. The more car you buy, the more you pollute. Keep some of the following in mind.

■ Smaller cars pollute less than large ones. They have smaller engines that get better mileage, and when the car is ready to be junked, there is less car to be disposed of.

■ A car that doesn't weigh a lot doesn't need power steering and power brakes. These add to the costs of running a large car.

■ The less fuel your car burns per mile of operation the less fuel that has to be drilled for and transported. Regardless of the other pollutants, less fuel consumption means less carbon dioxide.

■ Most cars are vastly overpowered. There is absolute-ly no need for anything but a race car to go 100 miles an hour.

■ Small cars cost less.

■ The low–powered cars use lower–octane gasoline which is likely to contain less lead.

■ Cars with automatic transmissions are said to emit fewer pollutants than those with manual shifts.

■ Cars with fuel–injection systems (VW, Porsche, Volvo, Mercedes) are better at feeding the proper mixture of gas and air to each cylinder than those with carburetors.

■ Buy a car that has an advanced pollution–abatement device that works.

■ Keep on the lookout for cars with power plants that are inherently less polluting than today's internal combustion engines.

■ Gadgets such as power windows, power antennas, power seats, and others add to the amount of energy your motor must deliver. In addition, the small motors that run these power devices are usually too hard to reach when the car is demolished for scrap. The copper in the electric motors contaminates the scrap and greatly reduces the value of the car hulk.

■ Air conditioning also adds considerably to the power requirements of your car (about 5 to 10 horsepower). Fuel consumption is higher and so are most other maintenance costs. Unless you live in a climate that demands one and you do a lot of driving there, buy a car with a light-colored roof and tinted window glass and be glad of all of the money you are saving. (Note: a true air conditioner costs three to five hundred dollars installed, two to three hundred dollars for the add-on models.)

■ Used cars should be looked at very carefully from the point of view of emissions. If it is possible to test the emissions level, do so. Cars produced before 1966 generally have much higher emissions levels. Conversion kits are available to cut down on their pollution levels.

■ Some low-powered cars and motor bikes have a two-cycle engine that uses a gasoline-oil mixture for fuel. These tend to have visibly high particulate and hydrocarbon emissions.

Your present car

There are a number of ways you can act now to keep your car's contribution to air pollution down.

■ Drive sanely. Jack–rabbit starts and high speeds drastically increase gasoline consumption and pollution. Fuel consumption and tire wear are 50% higher at speeds of 70-80 mph than at 50. Don't let your engine idle if you can avoid it. Professional drivers in economy runs manage to cut gasoline consumption markedly using these techniques.

■ Keep your car in good repair. Being on time with oil changes and lubrication will postpone the time that your car will burn oil. A well–tuned car (every 6000 miles) will emit far less pollution. A dead sparkplug can push emissions to 10 or 15 times over legal limits.

■ Make sure that your air pollution control device is connected and that your car is being tuned as it should be with the device.

■ Watch for gasoline leaks. Hydrocarbons that escape from a leaky tank or carburetor are just as harmful as those that come out of the tailpipe.

Your car's tires. When you buy a tire, you buy a lot of pollution. This is true of almost any manufactured product. Making a tire involves the textile, chemical, and rubber industries; all three are major polluters. Then as the tire wears down, the worn rubber is slowly released into the environment. At the end of the tire's life, it is too often just abandoned.

What should you do? Buy tires, but then drive in such a way that they will last. Avoid screeching starts and stops. Drive at moderate speeds, for tire wear is much greater at high speeds.

Some tread designs are quieter than others. If you can find a way to determine which ones are less noisy, buy that kind.

Don't buy studded tires for winter driving. The small carbide studs manage to chew up roads in a matter of two to five years and can cut the life span of a highway surface by as much as 75%. This gets expensive. While they may help you stop more quickly under certain conditions, they also tend to wipe out the painted road safety markings in about three months. Thus, their total effect on highway safety is probably negative. They have been banned in some states.

Worn–out tires can be put to use. They have been chained together and sunk to the bottom of the ocean to provide anchor points for artificial reefs. They have been "chewed up" and used as an ingredient in asphalt. And the recent news is that Firestone is building a plant that will be able to convert a ton of scrap tires into 140 gallons of liquid oils, 1500 cu. ft. of natural gas, and a solid residue that may have commercial uses. If the process proves economically feasible, they will build plants around the country.

When the old mare dies. All cars eventually reach the end of their usefulness. If you happen to own one which reaches this stage, make sure that it gets to an auto wrecker who will make proper use of it. If the car is not very old, there is probably an active market for its parts. A late–model vehicle with many salable parts is probably worth $500 to $1000.

In addition to its parts value, any car has potential scrap value. A Bureau of Mines study of 15 autos manufactured between 1954 and 1965 indicated the following quantities of metals:

2532 lbs. steel
511 lbs. cast iron
32 lbs. copper
54 lbs. zinc
51 lbs. lead

In some cars there is also a good bit of aluminum. About 28% of the scrap value is in the non–ferrous scrap.

A national survey has indicated that 38% of auto wreckers' acquisitions come from individuals. If you have to dispose of a car, pay attention to the methods the wreckers use. If you have a choice, pick one that a) will sell the reusable parts for their replacement value, b) won't pollute the air by burning the hulk to get rid of the 10% solid waste (tires, upholstery, glass), c) doesn't pollute the landscape with rusting hulks and old tires, and d) has an orderly operation that makes full use of the value in the junked car.

There are about 10,000 auto wreckers in the business, many of them rather small operators. Some have access to the expensive equipment that makes processing of cars efficient and profitable—the smokeless incinerators, balers, shredders, and shearers—and some don't.

OTHER WAYS TO HELP

Thus far, this chapter on transportation has concentrated on two topics—the choice among various modes of travel and the selection and operation of an automobile. In so doing, we have covered many of the major transportation decisions that you face, but there are more ways that you can make a contribution to environmental health.

Car pools and offering rides

Surveys have shown that the average load in the private automobile is in the range of 1.2 to 1.5 passengers in a vehicle that will hold between 4 and 6 comfortably. Clearly, one of the ways to reduce pollution and fuel consumption is to fill up the cars that will inevitably be on the road. Then we wouldn't need as many cars to carry the same number of people.

The car pool is a good way of accomplishing this. If you have no choice but to drive to work and you know others who live nearby with whom you can make such an arrangement, do so. In this way, you can cut down on operating expenses, help to alleviate traffic congestion, and free the car you leave at home for more active service. It might make it possible to get along comfortably with one less car in the household.

Car pools can have an effect. During Earth Week, April 1970, a San Francisco radio station launched a one–day car pool experiment that reduced the morning traffic load across the Golden Gate Bridge by about 6%. In San Francisco and other cities, the suggestion has been made that car pools be encouraged by charging admission to the city, with reduced fares for cars that are full.

You don't have to be part of an organized car pool to share the space in your car.

■ The next time you drive to a meeting, offer a ride to a friend or ask for a ride from a friend.

■ Make your trip to the shopping center with a friend.

■ If you are going to take a long trip by car and you have space for a rider, find one. Check with friends well in advance of departure, or look at the notices on college bulletin boards.

■ Unless you are really uptight about it, don't be afraid to offer a ride to a stranger. Hitch–hiking is common in Europe, especially among the offspring of affluent Americans.

Make your second car a bicycle

Consider the advantages that the bicycle has to offer— low cost, no pollution, and convenient to park.

■ For under $50 you can get a bicycle fitted with enough trimmings to make it practical for going shopping and carrying a small child. The cheapest car costs about thirty times that.

■ A bicycle is also inexpensive to operate, maintain, and insure.

■ Bicycles are quieter than any form of motorized transportation, produce no pollution, and use up no fuel.

■ A bicycle takes up about 1/30th the parking space of a car.

■ In city traffic today, the bicycle is often faster than the car or bus.

■ Bicycles give the rider the sort of healthy exercise that many Americans usually do not get.

■ Riding a bicycle makes it possible to get a better appreciation of a beautiful day, or a pleasant ride through the park.

It cannot be disputed that riding a bicycle also gives you a better appreciation of a rainy day and the foul exhaust from polluting vehicles that share the road with you. It is not without its drawbacks. Yet even within our foulest cities, intrepid souls rely on bicycles and enjoy them. *The New York Times* quoted a 32–year–old millionaire who pedals up Fifth Avenue to social engagements in a dinner jacket as explaining, "It's much easier than fussing with a chauffeur."

Even if you don't use a bicycle every day of the year, you should have one for the times when you can use it. Many of the short trips you take each day—for a newspaper, to visit a neighbor, to pick up an item or two at the grocery store—could be done by bicycle. Even major shopping can be done by bicycle, if the store has a delivery service.

And when it is time for a joy ride, put the family on bicycles instead of packing them into a car. If you have to travel some distance to find nice riding, take the bicycles along and park the car while you enjoy the ride. Even VW owners can do this—a bicycle rack that attaches onto the back of the car can be bought. Once upon a time railroads also offered bicycle piggy—back service. There may be some that still do.

Walk

The most natural form of locomotion, walking has been in use since before the invention of the wheel and the discovery of fire. Reliable and totally non–polluting, it offers convenience—no parking, no cost. Invigorating, it promotes health and gives you the chance to think.

14. RECREATION: LEISURE USE OF LEISURE TIME

14. Recreation: Leisure Use of Leisure Time

The stereotype of the modern man at leisure portrays him either seated in front of a television set (250 watts) with a disposable can of beer in hand or at the controls of a high–powered vehicle speeding around some part of his environment. The latter reflects an unfortunate tendency to carry the hectic pace of our professional and working lives into our outdoor recreation.

However, a wide range of activity can be found between absolute torpor and superkinetics.

NON-POWERED RECREATION

Spend your leisure time in ways that do not involve the use of power.

■ Spend some time on your garden. It will repay you with beauty and with wholesome vegetables and will help you to learn how ecologically together systems work.

■ Discover walking. Get to know your neighborhood and discover its parks and pleasant spots. It is a good way to collect your thoughts and get some exercise.

■ Take up hiking. Get together with some friends, pack a small lunch or picnic, and take short walking trips on weekends. Get to know the parks and countryside near your home.

■ Instead of hopping into the car for a joy ride on a beautiful day, get on a bicycle and go for a non–polluting spin. If you must get away from the city to make this pleasant, buy a bicycle rack for your car.

■ Go camping. Try the real thing without all of the amenities. It is the best way to gain a full appreciation of the outdoors.

It isn't wise to go camping or backpacking (carrying everything you need in a pack on your back) unless you know what you are doing or are with someone who does.

Choosing the right site at the right time of year, judging the stamina and abilities of the campers, planning the menu, selecting enough but not too much clothing and equipment, and providing adequate shelter and safety are all critical decisions that require some prior experience.

If everything is properly worked out, however, camping and backpacking can introduce you to great, unspoiled country that you would never experience any other way. It is an exhilarating experience that will draw you back for more.

With a good pair of hiking boots, a sleeping bag (or roll), a polyethylene–tube tent, a tin cup and a spoon plus other things that you can scrounge at home or borrow you can join a camping trip and begin a camping career. A pack and other equipment can be bought as you gain experience and need it. If you are a complete novice, it would be wise to contact a local conservation organization that runs trips, such as the nearest chapter of the Sierra Club or the Appalachian Mountain Club. Or contact the outing club at your local college.

■ Take an active interest in the biology, ecology, and geology of the areas that you visit. It is a good way to deepen your appreciation of the outdoor experience. There are a number of excellent field guides to just about anything you might be interested in.

■ Participate actively in some sport instead of forever being a spectator. Join a team or take up an individual sport such as tennis or golf.

■ Those who would buy a power boat should buy a canoe, a kayak, or a sailboat instead. Those who would buy a snowmobile should buy a pair of snowshoes or cross–country skis. The non–motorized counterparts have the advantages of costing less, providing much more healthful exercise, and bringing the user into a much closer relationship with the natural environment he is visiting.

PROTECT THE ENVIRONMENT

The natural environment is both fragile and resilient. It is easy to destroy its purity, but it is difficult to overwhelm it. If natural places are treated with respect, they hold up pretty well and have a fairly large carrying capacity.

■ Machines such as trail bikes, motorboats, and snowmobiles are too often used to abuse the environment. Willfully or unintentionally, many people use them to harass wild animals, to destroy the peace and quiet of the wilderness, and to bring litter and pollution into environments that have been clean and free of the most undesirable aspects of man. There are certain areas that should remain forever free of any sort of motorized vehicle. Respect them.

■ Don't litter. It used to be said that tin cans should be buried so that they would rust, but so many have been that this is no longer wise. Everything that you carry in to a campsite should be carried out.

■ When camping it is frequently wise to carry your own stove and fuel. Areas in the high Sierra are so heavily used that there is no longer enough dead wood to enable you to forage for fuel.

■ If you own a cruising boat, equip it with a unit that will keep it from polluting the water. Boats now afloat discharge sewage equivalent to a city of 500,000 persons. Recent state laws requiring holding tanks have been a sore point with many boat owners who feel that action should first be taken against the large industrial polluters. Although pollution from the big boys is much greater than that from any individual boat, that fact is irrelevant. *Each* person must be willing to clean up his share *and* go after the worst polluters. If adequate pump—out stations are available, the holding tank is preferable to units that "treat" the sewage on board and then dump it overboard.

Fuel spills are another environmental hazard that boat owners must be especially careful of.

WILDNESS AND SAVING THE ENVIRONMENT

It is only through recreation that a large portion of our urban population has any significant contact with the natural life–support system that sustains life on the earth. It isn't as easy to see the bad effects of pollution in an urban environment—where it almost seems natural—as it is in a natural setting. Yet it is in the non-urban ecosystem that the ecocatastrophe that will destroy mankind is beginning.

Thus, it is essential that all people have a chance to experience wildness and the real world in some measure. Cleaning up a stream, a river, or a marsh makes sense when one has a firsthand knowledge of what is there to be saved. Only when more people comprehend what conservationists and organic farmers have understood for some time will our society understand the wisdom of bringing its consumer decisions, indeed its whole life style, back into harmony with the natural environment.

IMPLEMENTING THE IDEAS IN THIS BOOK

Ideally, everyone should grow up with an understanding of what it means to live ecologically and how to do it. However, years of living unecologically, urbanization, and advertising have almost bred into us a combination of habits and attitudes that we must work to overcome.

For some the conversion of life style to one more ecologically harmonious with the environment is a slow evolution, each step preceded by an intellectual awareness; while for others it is more like a religious conversion. The resolve may be spurred by a vacation trip, an illness, or a simple discovery of how bad things have gotten.

Begin the conversion yourself. Start today. Begin in the home and at the market using some of the ideas in this book. Conserve power and water and paper and metals. Look for products that come in returnable packages. Find a market for your used newspapers. Begin to say no to some of the products that are ecologically unsound— *simply don't buy them.*

Beyond the dollar vote

If you really want to make an impression, however, you will want to take your consumer action beyond the dollar vote. Patronize the good products, but also publicize them—and the bad ones. Tell your friends. Convert the store managers. Write the manufacturers and explain that you are boycotting their product, why, and how they can get you back. The manufacturer's address is usually on the package.

When you find an advertisement offensive, contact the advertiser or the medium through which the ad appeared. Call the television or radio station or pen a note to the magazine or newspaper.

If you have been cheated, contact the Better Business Bureau and the consumer agency or attorney general's office of your local or state government. Another approach can be made through the President's Assistant for Consumer Affairs, now Mrs. Virginia Knauer, whose address is Executive Offices, The White House, Washington, D.C. 20025. Still another approach is to contact a consumer advocate such as Consumers Union or Consumers' Research.

Communicate your concern about environmental and consumer matters to your elected representatives. Ask that they support legislation calling for full disclosure of contents and adequate labeling of dangerous products.

Band together with other concerned consumers. There is a growing cooperative movement. Also, established conservation groups and new ecology action groups are becoming interested in consumer matters as they relate to the quality of the environment.

Become well informed about environmental matters. Ask questions and don't accept pat answers. Above all, be willing to think.

Appendices

Appendix I. Bibliography

CHAPTER 1.   INTRODUCTION

Bibliography

De Bell, Garrett, ed., *The Environmental Handbook*. New York: Ballantine, 1970. 95¢.

Rienow, Robert and Leona Train, *Moment in the Sun*. New York: Ballantine, 1967. 95¢.

Commoner, Barry, *Science & Survival*. New York: The Viking Press, 1966. $1.65.

Ehrlich, Paul R., *The Population Bomb*. New York: Ballantine, 1968. 95¢.

Odum, E., *Ecology*. New York: Holt, Rinehart, 1969. $3.25.

Kormondy, E., *Concepts of Ecology*. New York: Prentice–Hall, 1969. $2.95.

Whole Earth Catalog. Portola Institute. $3.00.

CHAPTER 2.   SHELTER

Bibliography

McHarg, Ian, *Design with Nature*. Natural History Press, 1969. $19.95.

Whyte, William, *The Last Landscape*. New York: Doubleday, 1968. $6.95. Also available in paperback.

Schuberth, Christopher J., "Barrier Beaches of Eastern America," in *Natural History* magazine, June-July, 1970.

Leopold, Luna, "Let's Sing 'Auld Lang Syne' for the Upper Brandywine" in *Natural History* magazine, June-July, 1970.

References

Consult the *Consumer Bulletin Annual* and *The Buying Guide Issue* of *Consumer Reports* for articles on "Gas, oil, and electric heating equipment" and "Heating the house".

Consumers All, The Yearbook of Agriculture, 1965, U.S. Department of Agriculture. $2.75.

This book contains a good bit of useful information. But read it carefully because most of the articles are not written from an ecological point of view. Some of the advice is not good.

"Where Not to Build: a guide for open space planning," *Technical Bulletin 1, Bureau of Land Management,* U.S. Department of the Interior. $1.00.

Simple Plumbing Repairs, Farmer's Bulletin No. 2202, U.S. Department of Agriculture. 10¢.

Home Heating: Systems/Fuels/Controls, Farmers' Bulletin No. 2235, U.S. Department of Agriculture. 30¢.

Heat Pumps for Heating and Cooling Homes, Agriculture Information Bulletin No. 306, U.S. Department of Agriculture. 10¢.

Equipment for Cooling Your Home, Home and Garden Bulletin No. 100, U.S. Department of Agriculture. 5¢.

"Federal Involvement in Hazardous Geological Areas," *Hearings* before a subcommittee of the Committee on Government Operations of the House of Representatives, May 7 and 8, 1969 and *Report* of August 6, 1969.

CHAPTER 3.   THE LAND AROUND YOUR SHELTER

References

"Attracting Birds," *Conservation Bulletin No. 1,* Fish and Wildlife Service, U.S. Department of the Interior. 15¢.

"Air Pollution Detectives," in *Science for Better Living,* The Yearbook for Agriculture, 1968, U.S. Department of Agriculture. $3.00.

CHAPTER 4.   GARDENING: WEEDS AND PESTS

Bibliography

Rudd, Robert, *Pesticides and the Living Landscape.* Madison: University of Wisconsin Press, 1964. $1.95.

Graham, Frank, Jr., *Since Silent Spring.* Boston: Houghton Mifflin Co., 1970. $6.95.

Carson, Rachel, *Silent Spring*. Fawcett, 1962. 95¢.

Whiteside, Thomas, *Defoliation*. New York: Ballantine, 1970. 95¢.

Darlington, Jeanie, *Grow Your Own*. Order from The Bookworks, 1611 San Pablo Avenue, Berkeley, California 94702. $1.75.

Stout, Ruth, *How to Have a Green Thumb Without an Aching Back*. New York: Simon & Schuster. $1.45.

Rodale Press of Emmaus, Pennsylvania 18049 publishes a monthly magazine *Organic Gardening & Farming* which is always fun and informative reading. Rodale has also printed a wide variety of books and pamphlets which span the needs of beginners and old hands. Write them for a complete listing. The following is a selection of some of the books and pamphlets relevant to this chapter.

How to Grow Vegetables & Fruits by the Organic Method by J. I. Rodale & staff. $9.95.

Encyclopedia of Organic Gardening by J. I. Rodale & staff. $9.95.

Best Ideas for Organic Vegetable Growing by the staff. $4.95.

"Control Garden Pests" by J. I. Rodale & staff. A pamphlet.

"Organic Fertilizing" by the staff. A pamphlet.

"Make Compost in 14 Days" by the staff. A pamphlet.

"All About Mulch" by the staff. A pamphlet.

Organic Gardening & Farming. Subscription rate is 60¢ per issue, $5.85 per year.

Tirrel, Ruth, "Not many Pests in My Patch" in *Organic Gardening & Farming*, May, 1970.

Goldman, M. C., "Can We Control Pests Without Pollution?" in *Organic Gardening & Farming*, July, 1970.

"Minigardens for Vegetables," *Home and Garden Bulletin No. 163*, U.S. Department of Agriculture. 15¢.

"Pesticides and Their Relationship to Environmental Health," *Report of the Secretary's Commission*, Department of Health, Education, and Welfare, chaired by Emil M. Mrak. December 1969. $3.00.

"Pesticides: What's Safe?" Massachusetts *Audubon Newsletter*, May-June 1970.

"Weed Killers" in *Consumer Reports*, June 1970.

"Garden Insecticides" in *Consumer Reports*, July 1969.

Linford, Lloyd, "You Can Buy Nerve Gas in the Grocery Store" in *Earth Times,* July 1970.

CHAPTER 5. CONSUMING ENERGY IN THE HOME

References

"Planning Your Home Lighting," *Home and Garden Bulletin No. 138,* U.S. Department of Agriculture. 20¢.

The reader is referred to the monthly and annual issues of *Consumer Reports* and *Consumer Bulletin.* The articles published there contain a considerable amount of relevant information, specifically, information on electric and water consumption of the various models of some appliances.

CHAPTER 6. WATER USE IN THE HOME

References

"The Cost of Clean Water," Federal Water Pollution Control Administration, U.S. Department of the Interior, 1968. A multivolume study, industry by industry.

"A Study of Residential Water Use," Federal Housing Administration, U.S. Department of Housing and Urban Development. 55¢.

Bradley, Charles C., "Human water needs and water use in America" reprinted from *Science* (October 26, 1962) in *Readings in Conservation Ecology,* George W. Cox, ed., New York: Appleton-Century-Crofts, 1969.

Commoner, Barry, "Soil and Freshwater: Damaged Global Fabric" in *Environment,* April 1970.

CHAPTER 7. MANAGING WASTE IN THE HOME

Bibliography

"The Role of Packaging in Solid Waste Management, 1966 to 1976." *Public Health Service Publication No. 1855,* U.S.

Department of Health, Education, and Welfare, 1969. $2.25.

Schuler, Stanley, *How to Fix Almost Everything*. New York: Pocket Books, 1970. 75¢.

Regan, Tom, "There is no Away" in *Ecology: the journal of cultural transformation, Vol. 2*, Ecology Action Educational Institute, Box 9334, Berkeley, California 94709.

Olds, Jerome, "Recycle Paper and Save the Dump" in *Organic Gardening & Farming*, July 1970.

"Pollution Curbs on Papers Asked," *New York Times*, May 31, 1970.

"Central waste disposal: New service looks for some action" in *Environmental Science & Technology*, March 1970.

"Solid Wastes" in *Environmental Science & Technology*, May 1970.

CHAPTER 8. HOME ENVIRONMENTAL HAZARDS

References

Shurcliff, William A., *S/S/T and Sonic Boom Handbook*. New York: Ballantine, 1970. 95¢.

Brower, "Noise Pollution: A Growing Menace" in *Saturday Review*, May 27, 1967.

Bailey, "Noise Is a Slow Agent of Death" in *The New York Times Magazine*, November 23, 1969.

Curtis, Richard and Hogan, Elizabeth, *Perils of the Peaceful Atom*. New York: Ballantine, 1969. $1.25.

"A Sensible Look at Radiation from TV Sets," in *Consumer Reports*, September 1968.

"Some Observations on X–Radiation" in *Consumer Reports*, January 1970.

Aaronson, Terri, "Mystery" in *Environment*, May 1970.

Aaronson, Terri, "Out of the Frying Pan" in *Environment*, June 1970.

"Phosphates in Detergents and the Eutrophication of America's Waters," *Report of the Subcommittee on Conservation and Natural Resources of the House Committee on Governmental Operations*, April 14, 1970.
The *Hearings* were held on December 15 and 16, 1969. Both can be obtained from the subcommittee or the Government Printing Office.

CHAPTER 9.   FOOD FROM THE MARKET

References

Turner, James S., *The Chemical Feast*. New York: Grossman, 1970. 95¢.

Guide to Organic Foods Shopping and Organic Living. Emmaus: Rodale, 1970. $1.00.

Hunter, Beatrice Trum, *The Natural Foods Cookbook*. New York: Pyramid, 1961. 95¢.

Rombauer, Irma S. and Becker, Marion R., *Joy of Cooking*. Indianapolis: Bobbs-Merrill. $6.95.

Gibbons, Euell, *Stalking the Wild Asparagus*. New York: David McKay Company, 1962.

"Home Economics: Foods and Cooking," *Price List No. 11*, Superintendent of Documents, Washington, D.C. 20402. (Lists all government documents available in this area.)

"Composition of Foods," *U.S. Department of Agriculture Handbook No. 8*, 1963. $1.50.

"Pesticides: A report on residues in food," *FDA Papers*, June 1967. 25¢.

"Drugs in Animal Feed? A question without an answer," *FDA Papers*, September 1967. 10¢.

"An industrial waste guide to the Potato Chip Industry," *Public Health Service Publication No. 756*, U.S. Department of Health, Education, and Welfare, 1960.

"Current Practice in Potato Processing Waste Treatment," Federal Water Pollution Control Administration, U.S. Department of the Interior, October 1969.

The Role of Packaging in Solid Waste Management, 1966 to 1967. *Public Health Service Publication No. 1855*, U.S. Department of Health, Education, and Welfare, 1969. $2.25.

"Cost Components of Farm-Retail Price Spreads for Foods," *Technical Study No. 9*, National Commission on Food Marketing, June 1966. 25¢.

"Comparative Costs to Consumers of Convenience Foods and Home-Prepared Foods," *Marketing Research Report No. 609*, U.S. Department of Agriculture, June 1963. 55¢.

"Home Canning of Fruits and Vegetables," *Home and Garden Bulletin No. 8*, U.S. Department of Agriculture. 15¢

"Home Freezing of Fruits and Vegetables," *Home and Garden Bulletin No. 10*, U.S. Department of Agriculture. 20¢.

CHAPTER 10. COSMETICS AND TOILETRIES

References

Marples, Mary J., "Life on the Human Skin" in *Scientific American,* January 1969.

Stabile, Toni, *Cosmetics: Trick or Treat?,* New York: ARC Books, 1970. 95¢.

The Medicine Show by the editors of *Consumer Reports,* Mount Vernon, New York: Consumers Union, 1970. $2.

"Cosmetics and Toiletries" in the *Consumer Bulletin Annual.*

CHAPTER 11. BIRTH, LIVING, AND DEATH

Bibliography

Who Shall Live? A report prepared for the American Friends Service Committee, New York: Hill and Wang, 1970. $1.75.

Mead, Margaret, ed., *Hunger,* A Scientists' Institute for Public Information Workbook. Available from the Scientists' Institute for Public Information, 30 East 68th Street, New York, New York 10021, 1970. $1.00.

Birth Control Handbook. McGill Students' Society, 3480 McTavish Street, Montreal, Quebec, Canada.

CHAPTER 13. TRANSPORTATION: WHERE DOES IT GET US?

References

In *The Environmental Handbook,* Garrett De Bell, editor. New York: Ballantine, 1970. 95¢.

　　Cantor, Kenneth P., "Warning: The Automobile Is Dangerous to Earth, Air, Fire, Water, Mind and Body."

　　Mumford, Lewis, "The Highway and the City."

　　Stilley, Brenn, "The SST."

Shurcliff, William A., *S/S/T and Sonic Boom Handbook.* New York: Ballantine, 1970. 95¢.

"America's Lifelines: Federal aid for highways," *Bureau of Public Roads*, U.S. Department of Transportation, 1969. 35¢.

"The Search for a Low-Emission Vehicle," *Staff Report Prepared for the Committee on Commerce*, U.S. Senate, 1969.

"Federal Low-Emission Vehicle Procurement Act," *Joint Hearings before the Subcommittee on Energy, Natural Resources and the Environment of the Committee on Commerce, and the Subcommittee on Air and Water Pollution of the Committee on Public Works*, U.S. Senate, January 27, 28, and 29, 1970.

Purdy, Ken W., "The New Urban Car" in *Playboy*, May 1970.

Netschert, Bruce C., "The Economic Impact of Electric Vehicles: A Scenario" in *Bulletin of the Atomic Scientists*, May 1970.

Luce, Larry, "The Brief against Standard Oil" in *Earth Times*, June 1970.

CHAPTER 14. RECREATION: LEISURE USE OF LEISURE TIME

References

Brower, David, ed., *The Sierra Club Wilderness Handbook*. New York: Ballantine, 1968. 95¢.

Appendix II. Periodicals of Interest to the Environmentally-Concerned Consumer

Whole Earth Catalog   Portola Institute. $3.00

Consumer Reports   Consumers Union
256 Washington Street
Mount Vernon, N. Y. 10550
$6/year(monthly)

Buying Guide Issue published in December. $2.25 alone

Consumer Bulletin: Consumer's Research
Washington, New Jersey 07882
$8/year(monthly)

Consumer Bulletin-Annual published in September. $2.95 alone

Organic Gardening & Farming   Rodale Press
33 East Minor Street
Emmaus, Pa. 18049
$5.85/year(monthly)

Guide to Organic Foods Shopping and Organic Living $1.00

Plants & Gardens   The Brooklyn Botanic Garden
Brooklyn, N. Y. 11225
$2.00/year(quarterly)

Environment   Committee for Environment Information
438 North Skinker Boulevard
St. Louis, Mo. 63130
$8.50/year(monthly)

Science   American Association for the Advancement of Science
1515 Massachusetts Avenue, N.W.
Washington, D.C. 20005
$12.00/year(weekly)

Consumer Reports and Consumer Bulletin

The Consumers Union of 256 Washington Street, Mount Vernon, New York 10550, and Consumers' Research of Washington, New Jersey 07882, each put out an annual buying guide that is very useful—*The Buying Guide Issue of Consumer Reports* (December) and *Consumer Bulletin–Annual*

(September), respectively. While neither has an ecological focus, and while some of their recommendations are counter to the best interests of the environment, these annuals and the monthly magazines that are put out by the same people contain a large body of information that is useful in making ecologically sound consumer decisions.

Append:x III. Government Publications

The Superintendent of Documents, Government Printing Office, Washington, D. C. 20402, is the source of a wealth of information that is contained in government–published pamphlets, studies, reports, and hearings. As with most other sources, the information is seldom presented from a save–the–environment point of view. Most of the documents were prepared before the recent environmental awakening, and unfortunately some departments of our government have yet to awaken. Thus, there is in these sources a good bit of environmentally unsound advice. At the same time, if you apply your common sense and knowledge of the environmental crisis, you should find much of the information quite useful.

Documents must be ordered by catalog number or by exact title, and payment must be included with the order before anything will be shipped. The following is a selection of the PRICE LISTS that are available free, to assist you in finding what you want:

11   Home Economics
21   Fish and Wildlife
25   Transportation, Highways, Roads, and Postal Service
35   National Parks
38   Animal Industry
41   Insects
42   Irrigation, Drainage, and Water Power
43   Forestry
44   Plants
46   Soils and Fertilizers
48   Weather, Astronomy, and Meteorology
51   Health and Hygiene
51A   Diseases
58   Mines
68   Farm Management
72   Homes
86   Consumer Information

If you live near a large city, you may be near a Government Printing Office bookstore. You may also be able to obtain information by checking with the local office of the appropriate branch of the government. Check in the white pages of your telephone book under *United States Government*.

In many cases, documents can be obtained quickly by writing directly to the appropriate department in Washington, to the appropriate congressional committee, or to your own senator or representative.

Index